Unit Five Resource Book

McDougal Littell

THE LANGUAGE OF LITERATURE

GRADE SEVEN

McDougal Littell
A HOUGHTON MIFFLIN COMPANY
Evanston, Illinois • Boston • Dallas

Permission is hereby granted to teachers to reprint or photocopy in classroom quantities the pages or sheets in this work that carry a McDougal Littell copyright notice. These pages are designed to be reproduced by teachers for use in their classes with accompanying McDougal Littell material, provided each copy made shows the copyright notice. Such copies may not be sold, and further distribution is expressly prohibited. Except as authorized above, prior written permission must be obtained from McDougal Littell Inc. to reproduce or transmit this work or portions thereof in any other form or by any other electronic or mechanical means, including any information storage or retrieval system, unless expressly permitted by federal copyright law. Address inquiries to Manager, Rights and Permissions, McDougal Littell Inc., P.O. Box 1667, Evanston, Illinois 60204.

ISBN-13: 978-0-618-14668-0 ISBN-10: 0-618-14668-7

Copyright © 2002 by McDougal Littell Inc.
Box 1667, Evanston, Illinois 60204
All rights reserved. Printed in the United States of America.

10 11 12 - MDO - 09 08 07

Unit Five Personal Challenges

Unit Five Personal Challenges

Family and Community Involvement

OPTION 1 **Discussing**

Brainstorm Ways of Meeting a Personal Challenge

- **Purpose** To discuss ways to meet a new challenge
- **Connection** All of the selections in Unit Five illustrate the theme of meeting personal challenges.
- **Materials** writing paper, pencils, pens
- **Activity** To connect the unit theme to your child's life, sit down with him or her and discuss strategies for meeting new personal challenges. Talk about significant challenges that your child has faced in the past. Use the web to take notes about the strategies your child used to meet those challenges. Then discuss a significant challenge that your child will be facing in the near future. Using the notes on the web, talk about which strategies were successful and which were not. Focus on the positive and helpful strategies. Finally, brainstorm and add strategies to the web that might help with the upcoming challenge.

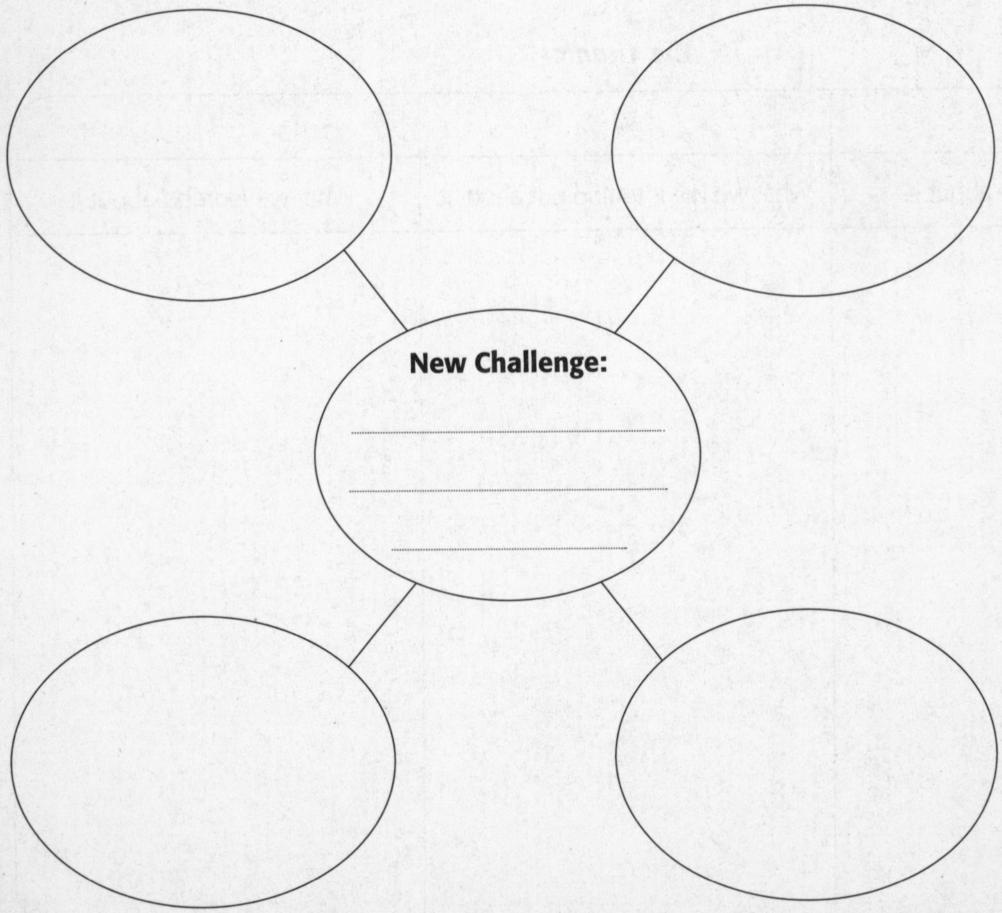

Family and Community Involvement

OPTION 2 Viewing

Watch a Documentary About the *Titanic*

- **Purpose** To learn more about the *Titanic*
- **Connection** The excerpt from *Exploring the* Titanic provides an account of a disaster involving a supposedly "unsinkable" ship.
- **Materials** Documentary video about the *Titanic*, a TV and VCR, a pencil or pen, writing paper, a ruler (optional)
- **Activity** Encourage your child to learn more about the *Titanic* by watching with him or her a documentary obtained from your local video store or library. (One such video is *Secrets of the* Titanic, a 1986 video by the National Geographic Society.) Help your child get the most out of the viewing experience by making a KWL chart like the one shown. Before watching the video, fill in the "K" and "W" columns. After watching, discuss what your child has learned and fill in the "L" column.

The *Titanic*

K	W	L
What we *know* about it	What we *want* to find out about it	What we *learned* about it

Unit Five Personal Challenges

Family and Community Involvement

OPTION 3 **Oral Reading**

Read Articles About Challenges

- **Purpose** To read about challenges
- **Connection** All of the selections in Unit Five illustrate the theme of people meeting and overcoming challenges.
- **Materials** current newspapers or news magazines, a pen or pencil, writing paper, a computer (optional)
- **Activity** To connect the unit theme to the world in which you and your child live, sit down with him or her and skim the headlines of current news articles for examples of people encountering or successfully overcoming personal challenges. When you find several appropriate articles, take turns reading them aloud. After reading, keep track of each article on a chart like the one shown. Encourage your child to talk about how reading about these people has helped him or her learn something about how people approach personal challenges.

Personal Challenges

Title of Article	What was the Challenge?	What Can We Learn from this Person's Approach?

from Exploring the *Titanic*

Robert D. Ballard

Summary

Setting: Early twentieth century; on board the *Titanic,* a passenger ship crossing the Atlantic Ocean

On April 10, 1912, the *Titanic* began its first trip from England to New York. At the time, it was the biggest ship ever built. The ship was thought to be unsinkable. Its passengers were divided by class on the ship. They included 17-year-old Jack Thayer and 12-year-old Ruth Becker. The first three days of the trip were smooth. On the fourth day, the ship hit an iceberg. Water poured into a hole in the bottom half of the ship. The *Titanic's* radio operators called for help. The nearest ship had turned off its radio. The crew began lowering lifeboats into the water at 12:45 A.M. Ruth Becker found a place in a lifeboat. More than fifteen hundred others stayed behind. By 2:05 A.M., the ship was sinking fast. Jack Thayer jumped off the ship as it slid into the water. He pulled himself onto an overturned lifeboat. Both he and Ruth watched the ship sink. Both were rescued at dawn. The rescue ship was called the *Carpathia.*

Name ______________________________ Date ______________

from Exploring the *Titanic* (page 658)

Active Reading SkillBuilder

Fact and Opinion

Facts can be proved. **Opinions**—personal feelings or beliefs—cannot. However, opinions supported by facts carry more weight than unsupported opinions. As you read the selection, note on this chart examples of facts, unsupported opinions, and opinions supported by facts.

Facts	Page Number
"In 1898, fourteen years before the Titanic sank, an American writer named Morgan Robertson wrote a book called The Wreck of the Titan."	660
Unsupported Opinions	**Page Number**
"Ruth Becker was dazzled as she boarded the ship..."	661
Opinions Supported by Facts	**Page Number**
"Everything was on a nightmare scale." Support: 882 feet long and high as an eleven story building	660

Name ______________________________ Date ______________

from Exploring the *Titanic* (page 658)

Literary Analysis SkillBuilder

Setting and Sources

Nonfiction authors may use **primary** and **secondary sources** such as photographs, descriptions from eyewitnesses, or artist's drawings to help them establish the setting of their article. As you read "Exploring the *Titanic*," look for descriptions in the story that are supported by a primary or secondary source. Record them in the chart, as shown below.

Setting Detail	Primary or Secondary Source That Supports Detail
p. 662 "Daylight shown through the huge glass dome over the Grand Staircase as jack went down to join his parents in the first-class reception room."	*p. 661 photograph showing the staircase.*

Name ______________________ Date ______________

from Exploring the *Titanic* (page 658)

Active Reading SkillBuilder

Accurate and Reliable Sources

Nonfiction writers must be careful that the people and documents from which they get their information—their sources—are reliable. An **accurate** source is a source that is free from errors. A **reliable** source is one that consistently gives a reader accurate information. To evaluate a source, look at the information it provides. Is it factual—can it be proved—or is it partly opinion? Can the factual information be double-checked against another source to be sure that it is accurate? Find five sources that Ballard used in creating his book. Explain whether you think the sources are accurate and generally reliable in the chart below.

Source	Accurate?	Reliable?
Writings of a survivor, page 664	*Yes, it is probably accurate. The description of the action could be checked by comparing it to other survivors' memories.*	*Yes, usually written accounts by eyewitness are reliable because the witness saw the situation with his or her own eyes.*

Name ______________________________ Date ______________________________

from Exploring the *Titanic* (page 674)

Grammar SkillBuilder: Independent Clauses and Compound Sentences

Key Concept: Writers use compound sentences to make their writing flow more smoothly.

Independent Clauses and Compound Sentences

A clause is a group of words that contains a subject and a verb. An **independent clause,** also called a **main clause,** can stand by itself as a sentence. **Compound sentences** are made up of two or more main clauses, joined by a coordinating conjunction like *and, or,* or *but*. Use *and* when you are joining two related ideas, *but* when the two ideas are contrasting, and *or* when the two ideas offer a choice. Place a comma before the coordinating conjunction.

Activities

A. Combine each of the following sentences using the appropriate conjunction.

1. The *Titanic* was eleven stories high. It had the biggest whistles in the world.
2. First-class passengers had the best of everything. Third-class passengers were crowded into compartments in the bottom of the ship.
3. Passengers wanting exercise could swim in the pool. They could use the rowing machines.
4. Harold Bride was the assistant wireless operator. He was pleased with his new job.
5. On Sunday, passengers might nap on deck. They might visit with friends.

B. Read each of the following sentences. Underline the subject(s) and verb(s) of the main clause(s) and write *compound* if it is a compound sentence.

1. The *Caronia* sent a warning about ice, as did the *Californian*. ____________
2. Harold Bride took a message to the bridge, and it was politely received. ____________
3. After trading stories with a friend, Jack Thayer walked around the deck. ____________
4. At 11:40 a lookout spotted an iceberg, and he told the duty officer about it. ____________
5. They tried to get out of its way, but they turned too late. ____________

Name ______________________________ Date ______________________________

from Exploring the *Titanic* (page 658)

Words to Know SkillBuilder

Words to Know

accommodations	eerie	indefinitely	novelty	toll
dazzled	feverishly	list	prophecy	tribute

A. Fill in each set of blanks with the correct word from the word list. The boxed letters will spell out a quality that the *Titanic* was famous for before it sailed.

1. This is how you do something when you are frantically trying to get it done. _ _ _ _ _ _ [ ] _ _ _
2. This is how you might feel when a lot of fireworks go off, especially if they're really great. _ [ ] _ _ _ _ _
3. This is how long something goes on when it goes on *and on and on.* _ _ _ _ [ ] _ _ _ _ _ _ _
4. This is something that's unusual but not *just* unusual. It's usually kind of creepy, too. _ [ ] _ _ _
5. This is what a pair of glasses would be if they had little wipers for when it rained. _ _ _ _ _ [ ] [ ]

Quality of the *Titanic:* ______________________

B. For each phrase in the first column, find the phrase in the second column that is closest in meaning. Write the letter of that phrase on the line.

______	1. a terrible toll	A. prevent a prediction
______	2. acres of accommodations	B. a large loss
______	3. a tremendous tribute	C. tilting tots
______	4. prohibit a prophecy	D. lots and lots of lodging
______	5. little lads who list	E. a huge honor

C. Write a news flash that might have been printed in a British newspaper about the sinking of the *Titanic* as soon as the news reached England. Use at least **three** of the Words to Know.

Name ______________________ Date ______________

***from* Exploring the *Titanic* (page 658)**

Selection Quiz

Recall the events in the selection. Then answer the questions in sentences or phrases.

1. What design elements were supposed to make the *Titanic* unsinkable?

2. What details early in the selection foreshadow the upcoming disaster?

3. What factors contributed to the *Titanic* hitting the iceberg?

4. Why was the loss of life so great?

5. Why do you think this disaster still captures people's attention?

Name ____________________ Date ____________________

The Lives of *La Belle* (page 675)

Active Reading SkillBuilder

Cause-and-Effect Chain

A series of events in which one event causes another event, and that event in turn leads to a third event, is called a **cause-and-effect chain.** Find the cause-and-effect chain on page 676 and write the events in the spaces provided.

Cause

↓

Effect/Cause

↓

Effect/Cause

↓

Effect/Cause

↓

Effect

Name ______________________________ Date ______________________

The Lives of *La Belle* (page 675)

Active Reading SkillBuilder

Structure and Text Organizers

The **structure** of an article refers to the way the information is presented, or organized, on the page. Most newspaper articles have a similar structure. Articles frequently contain **text organizers** such as titles, subheadings, photographs and captions to guide readers through the structure. Compare and contrast the use of text organizers in the newspaper article "The Lives of *La Belle*" with "Exploring the *Titanic*." Fill in the Venn diagram to help you see what the two articles have in common, and how they are different.

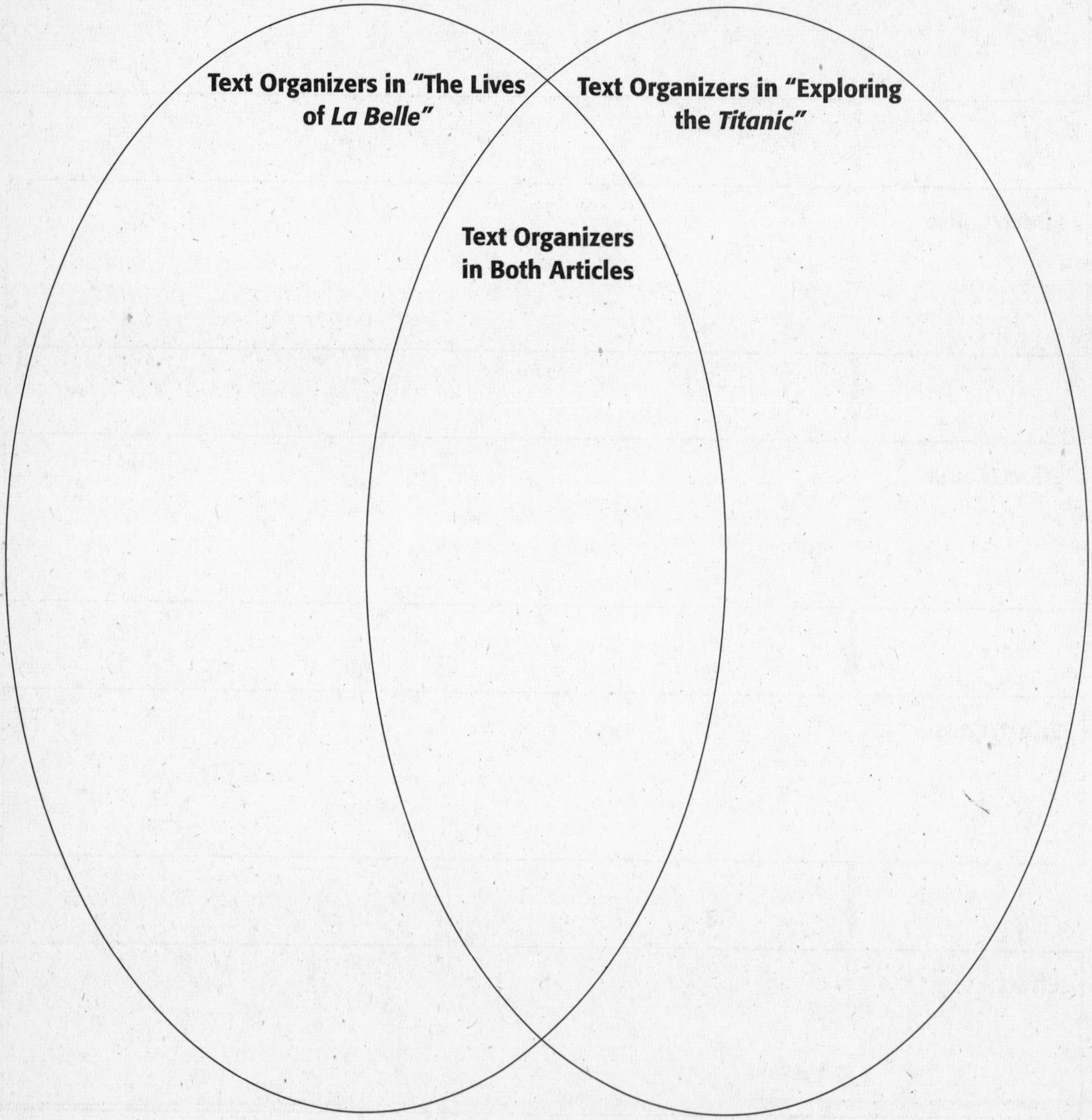

Last Cover

Paul Annixter

Summary

Setting: Hill country of the western Carolinas
Stan tells the story of his younger brother, Colin, and their pet fox, Bandit. The boys' father is a hunter and woodsman. He doesn't think highly of Colin's sensitive, artistic nature. After the boys raise Bandit, the fox returns to the wild. Colin tracks and watches his former pet. Neighbors' chickens start disappearing. Local hunters plan to kill Bandit. He outsmarts the hunters again and again. Finally, he is found and killed. Colin creates a wonderful drawing. It shows the fox hidden in his last hiding place. Colin and Stan found him there. The father sees that Colin shares his deep love and understanding of nature. He gains new respect for Colin and his art.

Name ______________________________ Date ______________

Last Cover (page 679)

Active Reading SkillBuilder

Visualizing

When you form a mental picture from a description, you are **visualizing.** This story has vivid descriptions. As you read, use this chart to note details that describe the setting. Then describe the mental picture you formed from the details.

Details from the Story	How I Picture Them
"The leafless woods were bleak and empty . . ."	*I picture a day with a gray sky and no leaves on the trees.*

Name ______________________________ Date ______________

Last Cover (page 679)

Literary Analysis SkillBuilder

Setting

The **setting** of a story includes the time and place in which it is set. Place refers to geographic region, type of landscape (mountains, desert, ocean), weather, urban or rural character, and customs, values, and beliefs of people in a location. Choose two descriptive passages from the story and write them below. Describe where each passage fits in the plot of the story. Then describe the drama each adds.

Description of Place		Where It Fits in Story		Drama It Adds
"It was late February, and I remember the bleak, dead cold that had set in, cold that was a rare thing for our Carolina hills."	→	Bandit has left, and the boys' father has just given a warning about his bad behavior.	→	It adds to the sad, hopeless feel of the story. The "bleak, dead cold" makes it seem like nothing can turn out well.
	→		→	
	→		→	

Follow Up: Look at your chosen passages. Could the story stand without either one, or are both essential to the telling?

Name ______________________________ Date ______________

Last Cover (page 679)

Literary Analysis SkillBuilder

Main and Minor Characters

A character is any person, animal, or imaginary creature in a story. The **main character** is usually the focus of the action in the story. **Minor characters** interact with the main characters in some way to move the action along, but typically aren't the focus of the story. To learn more about the characters of Colin and his father, work with two classmates. Take notes using the chart on this page as two group members read the parts of the story where Colin and his father discuss the fox. Note the traits shown by each character and the language or behavior that supports your observations.

	Colin	Father
Trait		
Evidence		
Trait		
Evidence		
Trait		
Evidence		
Trait		
Evidence		

Follow Up: What traits do Colin and his father have in common? How do these shared traits affect their relationship?

Name ______________________________ Date ______________

Last Cover (page 692)

Grammar SkillBuilder: Adverb Clauses of Time

Key Concept: Writers use adverb clauses of time to tell when an action occurs.

Adverb Clauses of Time

Adverb clauses of time tell when an action occurs and usually begin with a word or phrase such as *after, as, as long as, as soon as, before, during, since, until, when, whenever,* or *while.* If the adverb clause comes at the start of the sentence, add a comma after it.

Before he drew anything, Colin prepared another picture frame. (The adverb clause starts with *before* and modifies *prepared.*)

I watched **as Colin drew another picture.** (The adverb clause starts with *as* and modifies *watched.*)

Activities

A. Underline the adverb clause in each of the following sentences from the story.

1. After the fox made away with his first young chicken, Father suggested we name him Bandit.

2. It's always a sad time in the woods when the seven sleepers are under cover.

3. The boys meant a lot to Bandit while he was a kit.

4. Ever since I was ten, I'd been allowed to hunt with Father.

5. When he gets through with his spring sparking, he may come back.

B. Combine each pair of sentences by making one an adverb clause of time.

Example: Bandit left us. He was grown.
Rewritten: Bandit left us when he was grown.

1. Summer came on. Bandit began to live up to Father's predictions.

2. The dogs chased the wrong fox for twenty minutes. They realized their mistake.

3. The short day was nearing an end. I heard the horn sound again.

4. Bandit's secret had been Colin's since an afternoon three months before. He'd watched the fox swim downstream to hide in the deep pool.

5. Father sat holding the picture with a sort of tenderness for a long time. We glowed in the warmth of the shared secret.

Name ________________________________ Date ________________

Last Cover (page 679)

Words to Know SkillBuilder

Words to Know

bleak	essence	invalid	predestined	sanctuary
confound	harried	passive	sanction	wily

A. Match each description to the most appropriate Word to Know. Write the word next to the description.

1. This is another word for a person's true character. Colin's was artistic and thoughtful. ____________
2. Bandit may have felt this way after being chased and terrorized all day by hunters and dogs. ____________
3. The fox finally felt safe when he found this in an isolated, leaf-covered pool. ____________
4. This is one way to describe the dreary woods in the middle of the long, cold winter. ____________
5. Father used this word to label Colin, who often seemed sickly and unable to do much around the house. ____________
6. Whenever the hunters thought they had him, Bandit managed to do this to them with his tricks and hiding places. ____________
7. The boys' mother believed that Colin's fate might be already decided. In other words, she felt he was this. ____________
8. The boys' father described Colin's interpretation of nature in this way; Father preferred to experience nature in a more active, hands-on way. ____________
9. This is one way to describe Bandit's sly, clever nature. ____________
10. As someone who understood animals, the boys' father could not with a clear conscience do this to the idea of making a pet out of a wild animal. ____________

B. Retell part of "Last Cover" using **five** of the Words to Know.

Name ______________________ Date ______________

Last Cover (page 679)

Selection Quiz

Recall the characters and events in the selection. Then answer the questions in sentences or phrases.

1. Why does the family take in the baby fox?

2. What do Colin and his father have in common? How are they different?

3. How does the father feel when the hunters band together to kill Bandit?

4. How does Stan feel about his brother? What happens when they both discover Bandit's last hiding place?

5. When and how does the father realize the importance of Colin's artwork?

Name ______________________ Date ______________

Multiple-Meaning Words and Homonyms (page 693)

Building Vocabulary SkillBuilder

To find the correct meaning of multiple-meaning words and homonyms, use context clues or a dictionary. On the line, write a synonym or the correct meaning of each underlined word.

1. The sound of sirens jars me awake.

   Synonym / Meaning: ______________________

2. A fire has broken out on the seventh story of my building.

   Synonym / Meaning: ______________________

3. I get out of the building on my own, but I beam at the firefighters who are rescuing my neighbors.

   Synonym / Meaning: ______________________

4. I see that the firefighters have a keen understanding of their job.

   Synonym / Meaning: ______________________

5. The building is alight with the flames.

   Synonym / Meaning: ______________________

6. Some people stand on the fringe of the crowd, but one person brings hot drinks to those of us who got out.

   Synonym / Meaning: ______________________

7. One whole wing of the building burned.

   Synonym / Meaning: ______________________

8. Someone in my science class lived there, too.

   Synonym / Meaning: ______________________

9. "Don't you live on this block?" she said.

   Synonym / Meaning: ______________________

10. How did the fire affect you?

   Synonym / Meaning: ______________________

Opinion Statement

Prewriting

To develop your ideas for your opinion statement, try using a cluster diagram. Start by writing your opinion in the central oval below. In the other ovals, write related ideas that help develop or support your opinion. Add more ovals or lines to the diagram if you need them.

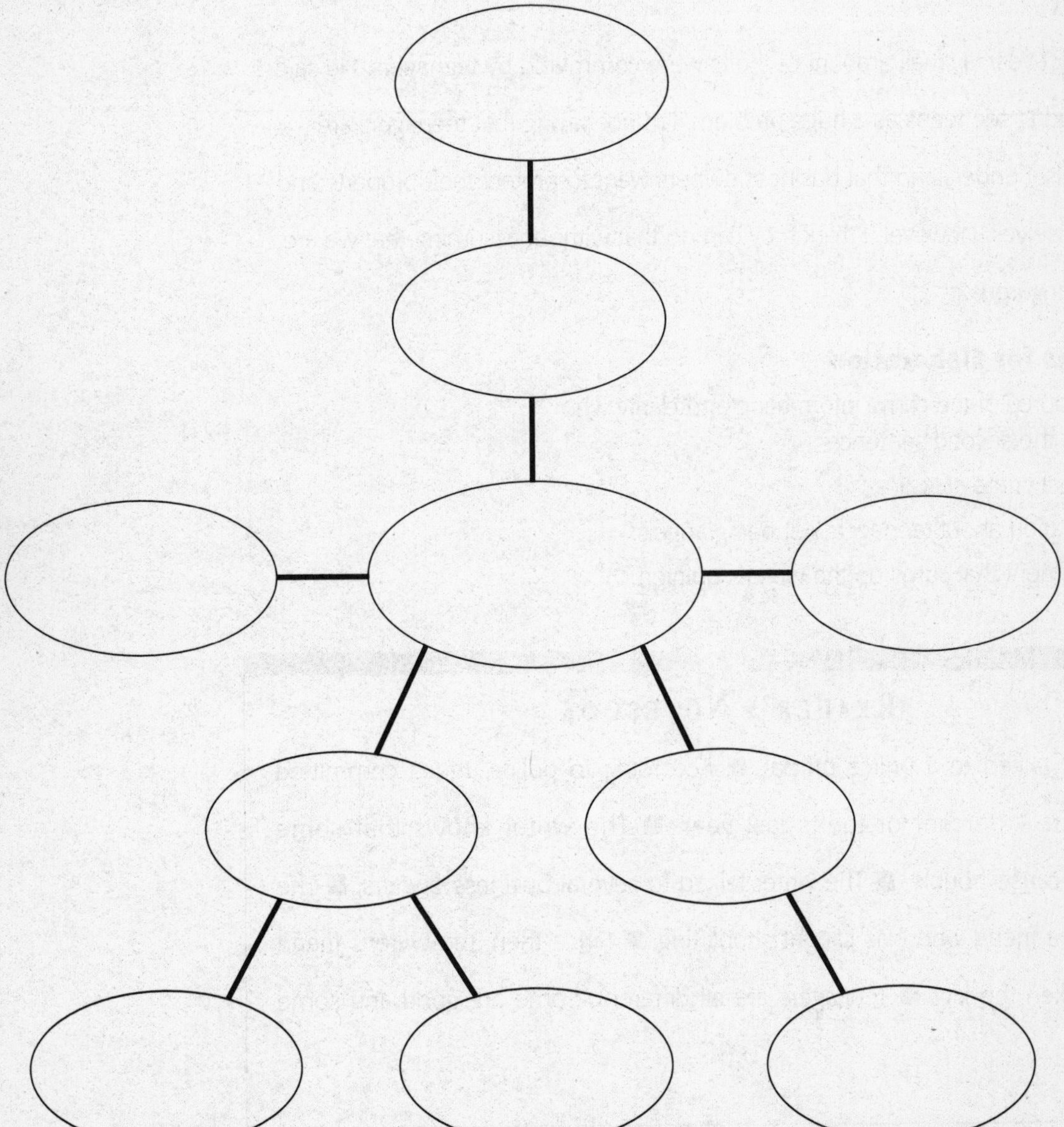

Opinion Statement

Drafting and Elaboration

After rereading the first draft of his opinion statement, one student realized that he had left out important information. Strengthen his writing by using the Reader's Notebook or your own ideas and following the Suggestions for Elaboration. Copy your revised paragraph on a separate sheet of paper.

Draft

Last year, a small amount of thefts were committed by teenagers. He said he didn't see teens as a huge problem. I'm not saying that teenagers are angels. I understand that business owners want to protect their property and themselves. However, I think they can do that without assuming that we are all dangerous.

Suggestions for Elaboration

- State the source of the crime information and clarify who the *he* is in the second sentence.
- Provide exact crime statistics.
- Add information about teenagers not being angels.
- Add a statement that sums up the writer's opinion.

Reader's Notebook

The writer talked to a police official. ■ According to police, teens committed fewer than 4 percent of thefts last year. ■ The writer knows that some teenagers cause trouble. ■ The writer talked to several business owners. ■ The writer has a friend who was caught shoplifting. ■ Since then, the writer's friend hasn't broken the law. ■ Teenagers are all different. Some are good and some are bad.

Opinion Statement

Peer Response Guide

When you write an opinion statement, you need to be careful that your own feelings do not interfere with your judgment. Sometimes someone else can help you detect mistakes in your reasoning. To check the soundness of your argument, ask a classmate questions like the following.

1. What is the issue that I am exploring in my paper?

   Response:

   Suggestions for Revision:

2. What don't you understand about the issue or about my opinion?

   Response:

   Suggestions for Revision:

3. Which parts of my opinion paper need additional support?

   Response:

   Suggestions for Revision:

Peer Response Guide continued

4. What is the strongest argument in my opinion statement?

Response:

Suggestions for Revision:

5. How did my opinion statement support or change your opinion of the issue?

Response:

Suggestions for Revision:

6. What action am I suggesting that people take?

Response:

Suggestions for Revision:

Opinion Statement

Revising, Editing, and Proofreading

TARGET SKILL ▶ Supporting your Opinion

As you revise your opinion statement, ask yourself the following questions:

- Have I adequately introduced the issue and my opinion?
- Have I used strong evidence to support my opinion?
- Does my evidence include facts and statistics?
- Do I anticipate and answer any questions the reader might have?
- Does my evidence help me to write a strong conclusion summarizing my opinion?

Editing and Proofreading

TARGET SKILL ▶ Punctuating Clauses

Use the suggestions given below to revise and proofread the following paragraph from the rough draft of one student's opinion statement. Then correct errors in grammar, usage, mechanics, and spelling using proofreading marks. Finally, copy your corrected draft onto a separate sheet of paper.

- Punctuate clauses correctly.
- Be sure that sentences are clear.
- Be sure lists of clauses make logical sense.
- Combine sentences to make writing less wordy.

Draft

I spoke with a police officer who said that he didn't see teens as a huge problem. He said teens commit a low percentage of crimes. He said he wants to make sure teens do not get hurt. He said he wants teens to learn the importance of obeying the law. I understand that some kids are rowdy. I know that some kids shoplift. I understand that some kids do get into trouble. But other kids hold down jobs do volunteer work and parents have taught their children to be responsible. Business owners want to protect their property and themselves. However, I think they can do that without assuming that we are all dangerous. If adults were to treat young people with respect they would see how respectfully we behave.

Applying

Now edit and proofread your own opinion statement. Refer to the bulleted list above.

Opinion Statement

Strong Student Model

Innocent Until Proven Guilty

Dear *Thirteen Magazine:*

1. Introduction states the issue and the writer's opinion.

Some stores in my town allow only two students inside at a time, especially the ones near the middle and high school. It seems that some adults think every student they meet fits the image of teens that they've gotten from newspapers or TV, which is an image of rowdy troublemakers. It's not fair! We're all different. A few of us might be mischievous troublemakers, but most of us are responsible and good.

2. Author uses persuasive argument to support the opinion and refute the opposition.

"You kids mess up the candy and magazines and then leave," says the owner of a convenience store. However, my parents taught me to clean up after myself, and so did my friends' parents. Neither I nor my friends have ever stolen anything.

3. Generates a list of supporting facts, examples, and statistics

According to Thelma Rodriguez, Director of County Volunteer Services, teens perform thirty percent of the volunteer work at local hospitals and rest homes. They work side by side with adults. Last year she had a list of seventy-five student volunteers. Thelma says she values the contribution of the teenagers, who often spend their only free time doing volunteer work.

Many students also hold jobs. Students who hold jobs have money, and they spend it. Maybe we should remind local business owners that students can be good customers.

4. Restates the opinion, using clear reasoning and respectful language

I spoke with a police officer, who said that last year fewer than four percent of thefts were committed by teenagers. He said he didn't see teens as a huge problem. I understand that business owners want to protect their property and themselves. However, I think they can do that without assuming that we are all dangerous. They should monitor us the same way they monitor adults, with video cameras and security devices. If adults were to treat young people with respect, they would see how respectfully we behave. Just like adults, teenagers are all different—both good and bad.

Thank you for the opportunity to express my opinion.

Sincerely,
Kyle Stevens

Opinion Statement

Average Student Model

Generation Gap

Dear *Thirteen Magazine:*

1. The introduction presents good ideas, but the issue and main argument are not clear.

Another Option:
• Keep the ideas presented in this paragraph, but end the paragraph with a clear statement of opinion.

Some stores in my town allow only two students inside at a time, especially the ones near the middle school. Do all adults think that every student they meet is right out of the newspaper or TV? We are not all rowdy troublemakers. Only some of us are, and they ruin it for the rest of us. That is just not fair!

"You kids mess up the candy and magazines and then leave," says the owner of a convenience store. He has a point. Some kids do. Sometimes I find a half empty can of soda pop on the shelves and I know some kid opened it, drank some, and left it. Those kids give us a bad name. We are punished for their actions. It makes me feel bad when I see something like that.

2. The author inadvertently supports the viewpoint the opinion statement is opposing. Focus should be on evidence that refutes the store owner's statement.

According to Thelma Rodriguez, Director of County Volunteer Services, teens perform 30 percent of the volunteer work at local hospitals and rest homes. She didn't say how many teens that was, however.

3. The author finds a loophole in the argument. The author should find substantial facts that support the opinion.

A few students also hold jobs. Not very good jobs, of course. It's even hard to get a good job with real responsibilities. That's another thing that is unfair. Students who hold jobs have money, and they spend it. Maybe we should remind local business owners that students can be good customers. The malls already fully understand that. Malls spend a lot of money on advertising to attract teens.

4. The opinion gets confusing as more issues are presented. Writer should stay focused on one issue.

I spoke with a police officer, who said that he didn't see teens as a huge problem. He mostly watches out for teens to make sure they do not get hurt and to help them understand the importance of obeying the law. I understand that business owners want to protect their property and themselves. However, I think they go a little overboard. It's their choice if they want to turn business away.

5. Writer includes good supporting details—such as the police officer's comments—but like the introduction, the conclusion is unclear. It does not clearly and reasonably express the writer's opinion.

Sincerely,
Kyle Stevens

Opinion Statement

Weak Student Model

Teenagers: My Opinion

Dear *Thirteen Magazine:*

Some stores in my town allow only two students inside at a time, especially the ones near the middle school. That is such a lame rule. Most adults stereotype kids as rowdy troublemakers. That is so unfair! Attitudes like that only make me angry. People behave in the way they are treated, and adults should treat kids with respect.

1. The language is very strong and charged with emotion. An opinion can be charged with emotion, but it must be grounded in fact and reason to win the reader's respect.

2. Again, this kind of argument and example could offend and alienate the reader.

"You kids mess up the candy and magazines and then leave," says the owner of a convenience store. Doesn't he know we mess them up because we know he thinks we're going to? He makes it like a dare and a challenge.

3. Although the example is good, the argument is ambiguous. The writer unintentionally reveals a questionable character.

The owner of another store in the area always says hello to me and smiles. She asks me how I'm doing. I would never do any damage to her store, and neither would any of my friends. She knows how to build good customer relations.

Maybe teenagers should boycott those stores who have that ridiculous rule. We should just not shop there. Teenagers are good customers. Malls know that. They encourage our business.

4. The essay is making another proposal instead of supporting an opinion.

I think the police don't really see teens as a huge problem. They just want us to understand the importance of obeying the law. Teen crime is exaggerated in the media. It makes business owners a little paranoid. They should just use their video cameras and security devices to watch us like they do everyone else, instead of imposing their made-up baby laws on us.

5. The essay does not contain statistics and facts.

Another Option:
- *Strengthen the opinion by using evidence that will persuade and convince the reader.*

6. Conclusion contains many opinions that are not supported with facts and that do not support the main point of the essay.

Sincerely,
Kyle Stevens

Opinion Statement

Rubric for Evaluation

Ideas and Content	Weak	Average	Strong
1. Clearly states the issue			
2. Clearly states an opinion on the issue			
3. Uses convincing examples, facts, and statistics to support opinion			
4. Uses clear reasoning to make convincing arguments			
5. Concludes with summary and restating of opinion			

Structure and Form			
6. Uses appropriate language			
7. Organizes the supporting evidence clearly			

Grammar, Usage, and Mechanics			
8. Uses correct grammar			
9. Uses correct punctuation, capitalization, and spelling			

Writing Progress to Date (Writing Portfolio)

The strongest aspect of this writing is ______________________________

____

The final version shows improvement over the rough draft in this way: ______________________________

____

____

A specific improvement over past assignments in your portfolio is ______________________________

____

A skill to work on in future assignments is ______________________________

Additional comments: ______________________________

____

A Crown of Wild Olive

Rosemary Sutcliff

Summary

Setting: Ancient Greece

Amyntas is a young man living in Athens. He is chosen to run in the Olympic Games. At the training camp, he meets Leon. Leon is from Sparta, a city state that is a fierce rival of Athens. The two become friends in spite of coming from rival cities. They find that they are competing in the same race. One day Leon cuts his foot. Amyntas has a brief, selfish thought. He thinks of his own victory if his friend can't run. Upset, he offers a bronze bull to Zeus. He prays, saying "Let me run the best race that is in me and think of nothing more." Leon's foot heals in time for the race. The boys line up before screaming crowds. Partway through the race, Amyntas and Leon are ahead of everyone else. Then the cut on Leon's foot reopens. Amyntas feels sorry for his friend. But he remembers his prayer and runs as hard as he can. He wins. Later he talks to Leon. Amyntas says that he might not have won if the cut on Leon's foot hadn't opened. Leon disagrees. "You ran the better race," he says. The games end and the boys part. They know that if they meet again, it will probably be in battle.

Name ______________________________ Date ______________

A Crown of Wild Olive (page 709)

Active Reading SkillBuilder

Cause and Effect

Two events have a cause-and-effect relationship when one event occurs as a result of the other. The event that happens first is the **cause,** and the result is the **effect.** Often, the event that was the effect becomes the cause of another event. As you read, use this chart to track the chain of cause and effect in this story.

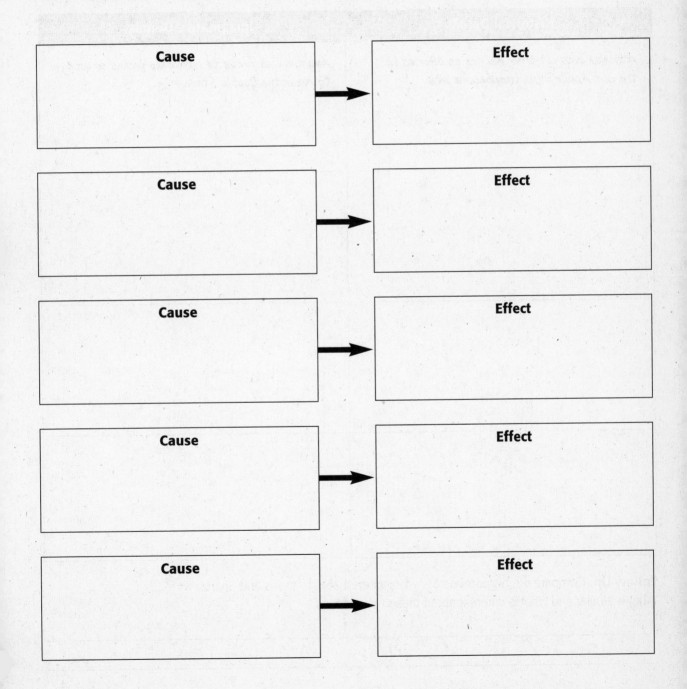

Cause		Effect
	→	
Cause		**Effect**
	→	
Cause		**Effect**
	→	
Cause		**Effect**
	→	
Cause		**Effect**
	→	

Name ______________________________ Date ______________

A Crown of Wild Olive (page 709)

Literary Analysis SkillBuilder

Historical Fiction

Historical fiction is fiction set in a past historical period. It combines details from the historical period in which it is set with fictional inventions. Sometimes historical fiction includes actual historical personages and events, but not always. Writers of historical fiction want the historical period to "come alive" for their readers. Use the chart below to record historical and imaginative details that occur in "A Crown of Wild Olive."

Historical Details	Imaginative Details
Athenian boys cut their hair as an offering to the god Apollo when they became men.	*Amyntas was proud to have been picked so young to run in the Double Stade.*

Follow Up: Compare the historical details you gathered about Athens and Sparta. What is similar and what is different about these two cultures?

____

____

Name ______________________________ Date ______________

A Crown of Wild Olive (page 709)

Active Reading SkillBuilder

Visualize

Vivid descriptions that appeal to the senses help readers **visualize,** or form mental pictures of, characters, events, and the story's setting. The descriptive details in "A Crown of Wild Olives" evoke strong images of ancient Greece, the young men, and the competition. Find descriptions in the story that help you visualize setting, characters, and events, and write them in the appropriate column of the chart.

Descriptions		
Setting	**Characters**	**Events**
". . .the white, dry heat of the Greek summer."		

Name ______________________ Date ______________

A Crown of Wild Olive (page 709)

Grammar SkillBuilder: Elaborating with Adjective Clauses

Key Concept: Writers use adjective clauses to add details to their writing.

Elaborating with Adjective Clauses

Adjective clauses contain a subject and a verb, like all clauses, and they modify a noun or a pronoun. Adjective clauses are always subordinate (or dependent) clauses: they do not express a complete thought and cannot stand alone as sentences. Adjective clauses often begin with *that, which, whichever, who, whoever, whom, whomever, whose,* or *of which.*

Leon, <u>who had been taught obedience from an early age,</u> was from Sparta.

The adjective clause is underlined. It modifies *Leon.*

Activities

A. Underline the adjective clause in each of the following sentences.

1. Amyntas waved farewell to his father, who had also been a runner.
2. The port that was closest to Olympia was five days distance from Athens.
3. The journey, which was his first, finally ended.
4. Early on, Amyntas met Leon, who was about the same age as he.
5. They walked among the booths, which had sprung up recently.

B. Rewrite each sentence, adding an adjective clause.

1. Leon cut his foot on something. ______________________
2. Amyntas cleaned and bound the foot. ______________________
3. The runners came from near and far. ______________________
4. The stadium was filled with spectators. ______________________
5. The race ended with Amyntas emerging as the winner. ______________________

Name ______________________________ Date ______________________

A Crown of Wild Olive (page 709)

Words to Know SkillBuilder

Words to Know

angular dappled reel substance unaccountably

A. Write the Word to Know that best completes each item.

1. If someone's body were slender and bony, you could describe it as _______________.

2. When you first get off a whirling carnival ride, you are likely to _______________ back and forth.

3. A horse with lots of spots is said to be _______________.

4. Something light, thin, and almost immaterial is said to be without _______________.

5. If there is no explanation for why something happens, it happens _______________.

B. Look at each pair of words and decide whether they are synonyms or antonyms. Circle your choice.

1. substance / matter	Synonyms / Antonyms
2. dappled / solid	Synonyms / Antonyms
3. angular / bony	Synonyms / Antonyms
4. unaccountably / understandably	Synonyms / Antonyms
5. reel / spin	Synonyms / Antonyms

C. Write a sentence in which you use any **three** of the Words to Know.

____

____

____

Name ______________________ Date ______________

A Crown of Wild Olive (page 709)

Selection Quiz

Recall the characters and events in the selection. Then answer the questions in sentences or phrases.

1. For how long have the Olympics been held as this story begins? What is unique in the region during the period of the games?

2. What promise does Amyntas make to his father as he departs for the games? Why is Amyntas's victory so important to his father?

3. What does Amyntas do when he has troubling thoughts about the race after Leon hurts his foot? Why?

4. Why does Amyntas consider letting Leon win the race? Why does he decide against doing that?

5. What does Leon wish for when he and Amyntas say goodbye? Why?

Name ______________________________ Date ______________

Passing on the Flame (page 728)

Active Reading SkillBuilder

Structure and Purpose

The **structure** of an article refers to the way information is laid out and organized on a page or screen. **Purpose** refers to the reason the article was written. Depending on its purpose, an article may use different structures. An article meant to entertain might have a title, subheadings, artwork, and a picture of the author. An informative article might have more photographs, captions, graphics such as timelines or charts, and boxes that pull out important quotes or facts. These text organizers and visual elements help guide the reader through the information. Look at the structure of the Web article on page 728 and the textbook article on page R4. Compare the structures by answering the questions below.

What is the purpose of each article? ______________________________

Web Article

1. What kind of text organizers does this Web article use?

____

2. How could you preview this article before you read it?

____

Textbook

3. What kind of text organizers does this textbook article use?

____

4. If you were reviewing this article for a test, which organizers would be most useful to you?

____

Comparison

5. What organizational elements do the two articles have in common? Why do you think these elements were chosen?

____

6. How does the content of the two articles affect the kind of organizational elements they have?

____

7. Which article do you find easier to follow? Explain you answer.

____

Name ______________________ Date ______________

Passing on the Flame (page 728)

Active Reading SkillBuilder

Monitor

Active readers **monitor** their use of reading strategies. As you read, make sure you are questioning, connecting, predicting, clarifying, visualizing, and evaluating. Complete the following chart by selecting one event from the story. In the center, write the topic and the page number on which it appears. Follow the strategy shown on each connecting line, and write your response in the box.

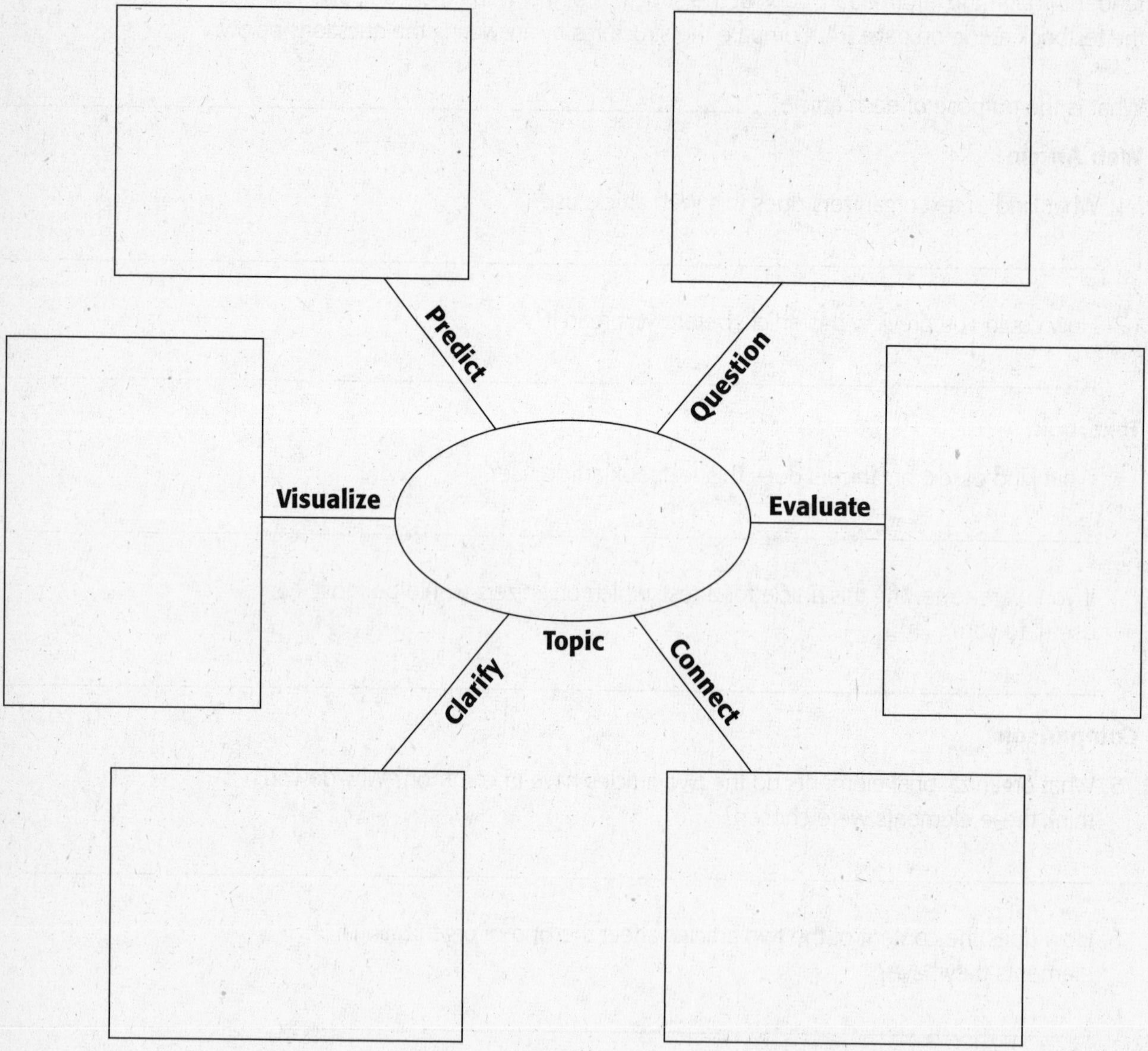

from Long Walk to Freedom

Nelson Mandela

Summary

Setting: South Africa, early twentieth century to the present

Nelson Mandela, first black president of South Africa, is a symbol of the fight for racial justice. The policy of apartheid, or racial segregation, under which South Africa was ruled for approximately half a century, created deep wounds among the people of that country. Mandela was inspired by early leaders against apartheid. These leaders reminded him that South Africa's greatest resource was its people. Mandela's own struggle against racism began when he joined the African National Congress in 1944. Because he advocated the end of apartheid, he was imprisoned for 27 years. While in prison, Mandela learned a very valuable lesson: anyone who takes away another's freedom is also a prisoner, a prisoner of prejudice and narrow-mindedness. After his release from prison, Mandela has continued his work for justice because, until all South Africans learn "a way that respects and enhances the freedom of others," his "long walk" must continue.

Name ______________________________ Date ______________

from Long Walk to Freedom (page 732)

Active Reading SkillBuilder

Main Idea and Details

The **main idea** of a passage is the writer's most important message. It may be stated directly, or may be implied. Choose one paragraph from the selection. Write the main idea and any supporting **details** on this chart.

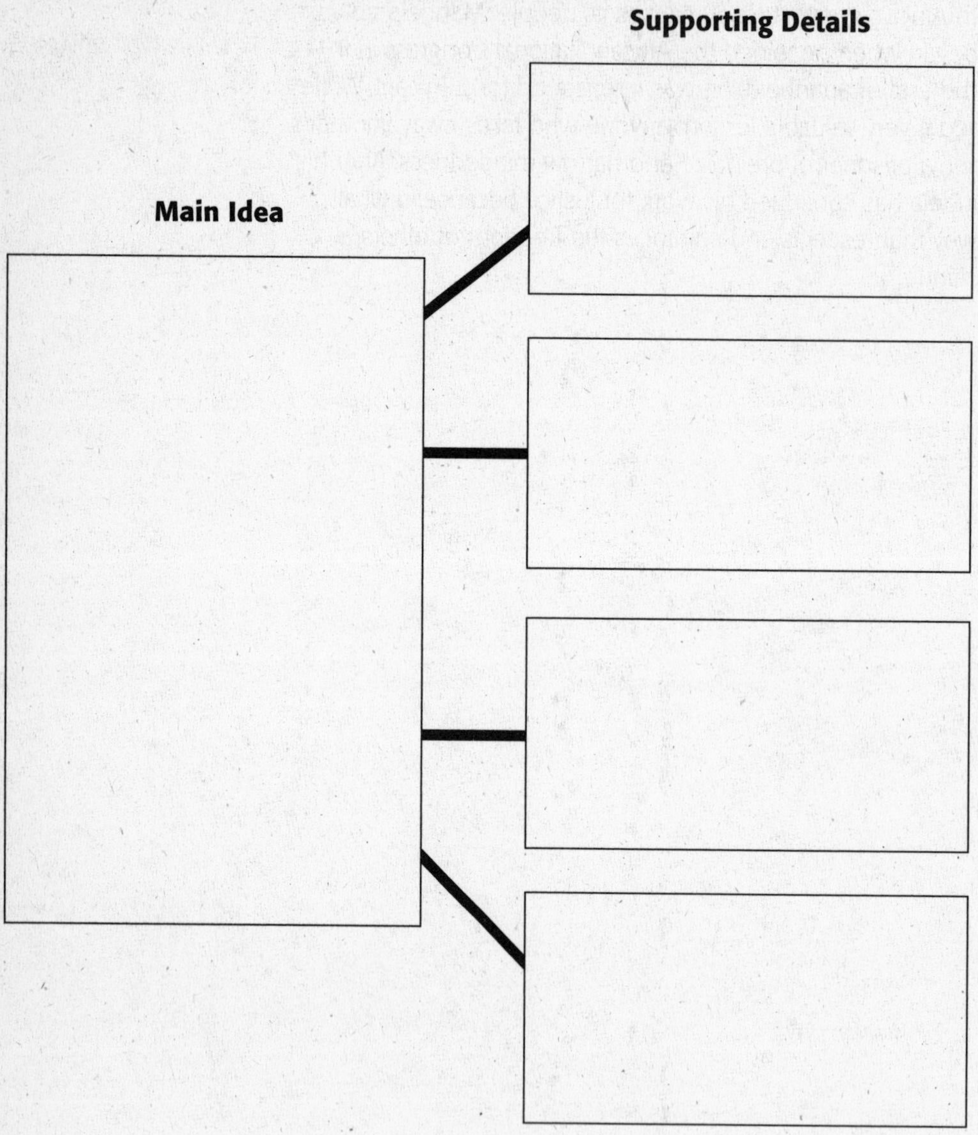

Name ______________________ Date ______________

from Long Walk to Freedom (page 732)

Literary Analysis SkillBuilder

Memoir

A **memoir** is a form of autobiography in which the person retells significant events in his or her life. As is the case with Nelson Mandela's memoir, these events may have a significance beyond the writer's own life. Use this chart to note significant experiences in Mandela's life and what he learned from them.

Experiences in Mandela's Life	What He Learned from Them

Follow Up: What are some differences between a memoir and a biography? How would this piece have changed if it were a biography rather than a memoir?

____

____

____

____

____

____

Name ______________________ Date ______________________

from Long Walk to Freedom (page 732)

Active Reading SkillBuilder

Author's Viewpoint

An **author's viewpoint** is his or her perspective on a particular subject. Experiences and personality can color how a person sees an event or person. Readers should try to determine what the author's viewpoint is in order to understand how that influences the author's writing. To begin identifying the writer's viewpoint, look for statements of personal belief. Write down statements of personal belief in the chart below and then explain what insight they give you into Mandela's viewpoint.

Statement	What it tells you about his viewpoint
"I have always known that its greatest wealth is its people, finer and truer than the purest diamonds."	*Mandela believes the citizens of his country are more important than South Africa's mineral wealth.*

Name ______________________________ Date ______________

from Long Walk to Freedom (page 739)

Grammar SkillBuilder: Using Adjective Clauses

Key Concept: Writers use adjective clauses to add information to their writing and to avoid choppy sentences.

Using Adjective Clauses

Adjective clauses modify nouns or pronouns and usually follow the word they are modifying. They usually begin with *that, which, whichever, who, whoever, whom, whomever, whose,* or *of which*. Clauses containing information essential to the meaning of the sentence are not set off with commas. Clauses without essential information are set off with commas. Clauses starting with *that* contain essential information; clauses starting with *which* generally don't.

The idea <u>that all people must be free</u> motivated me. (The adjective clause is essential to knowing what the idea is.)

My life, <u>which had once been my own</u>, was now dedicated to my people. (The adjective clause is not essential to knowing which life is being referred to.)

Activities

A. Underline the adjective clause in each of the following sentences. Add commas where appropriate.

1. My childhood which I loved had every appearance of freedom.
2. As a young man who had restrictions on his activities, I learned I was not free.
3. The freedom of everyone who looked like I did was curtailed.
4. I joined the African National Congress which fought to abolish apartheid.
5. My life which had been somewhat ordinary took a dramatic turn.

B. Combine each pair of sentences using an adjective clause.

1. In my absence my family suffered. It lasted for decades.

____

2. There were guards in prison. They showed some humanity.

____

3. The understanding came to me in prison. Everyone is hurt by racism.

____

4. I have never stopped believing in the idea. All people will one day be free.

____

5. I know that the people of South Africa will survive. They are its true hidden treasures.

____

Name ______________________ Date ______________

from Long Walk to Freedom (page 732)

Words to Know SkillBuilder

Words to Know

curtailed incomprehensible indivisible resiliency transitory

A. Complete each analogy with a Word to Know.

1. WONDERFUL : TERRIBLE : : understandable : ______________
2. HAPPY : CHEERFUL : : inseparable : ______________
3. BUOYANT : BUOYANCY : : resilient : ______________
4. LASTING : PASSING : : permanent : ______________
5. FIRE : EXTINGUISHED : : freedom : ______________

B. Using information from the selection, write up a mock interview with Nelson Mandela. Use all **five** Words to Know.

Interviewer: ______________

Mandela: ______________

Interviewer: ______________

Mandela: ______________

Interviewer: ______________

Mandela: ______________

Name ______________________ Date ______________

from Long Walk to Freedom (page 732)

Selection Quiz

Recall the characters and events in the selection. Then answer the questions in sentences or phrases.

1. How did Mandela's understanding of freedom change over the course of his life? What particular insight did he gain while in prison?

2. What does Mandela believe is South Africa's greatest resource?

3. What was Mandela's reason for joining the African National Congress?

4. Why does Mandela think oppressors need freeing?

5. What does Mandela say must happen in order for his people to be completely free?

Name ____ Date ____________________

The Elephant / The Turtle (page 740)

Active Reading SkillBuilder

Paraphrasing

When you restate a text in another form, or use other words to clarify the meaning of a text, you are **paraphrasing.** Unlike a summary, which is shorter then the original text, a paraphrase is often longer than the original. On page 743, you paraphrased one of the selection poems. Use the diagram below to paraphrase the other poem. Use the headings provided to help you, and remember to use your own words.

Poem: ______________________________

Main Ideas	Important Details

Paraphrase:

Name ______________________ Date ______________

The Elephant / The Turtle (page 740)

Literary Analysis SkillBuilder

Imagery

Words and phrases that appeal to readers' senses are called **imagery.** Vivid descriptions that appeal to the senses draw readers into a poem. Complete the following chart noting images from the two poems. Think about the effect these images have on you, and note how they helped you understand the poems.

"The Elephant"		"The Turtle"	
Image	**Effect**	**Image**	**Effect**
rope and chain	*It helped me to imagine how the elephant is being held captive.*	*breaking through "the blue-black skin" of the water*	*It helped me to see the stillness of the water.*

Follow Up: Select one of the poems and draw a picture using some of the images and effects you described above.

Name ______________________ Date ______________________

Researching Word Origins (page 745)

Building Vocabulary Skillbuilder

Use a dictionary to find out about a word's **origins,** and see if you can recognize other words from the same root. Look up each of the following words in the dictionary. Write its history and meaning in your own words in the chart.

Word	History/Origin	Meaning
apartheid		
twin		
freedom		
vista		
govern		
inkling		
fugitive		
gaze		
character		
nation		

from Anthony Burns: The Defeat and Triumph of a Fugitive Slave

Virginia Hamilton

Summary

Setting: Boston, Massachusetts, 1854

Anthony Burns is an escaped slave from Virginia. He is living in Boston when slave hunters capture him. Because of the Fugitive Slave Act, he will be returned to his master, Colonel Suttle. Under the law, however, Burns is allowed a hearing in a court of law. Anthony assumes there is no hope. He believes that he will be returned to his master and severely punished. Therefore he is hesitant to accept help from Richard Henry Dana, a lawyer. Dana is an abolitionist, however. Abolitionists are those who fight against slavery. Dana is determined to watch over the court proceedings for any hint of wrongdoing. Meanwhile, Theodore Parker and other abolitionists try to alert the public to Anthony's case. Many people living in Boston are devoted to protecting black inhabitants from bounty hunters. If they can interest concerned citizens in Anthony's case, they may be able to help him. The city of Boston sees Anthony as a symbol of the fight for freedom, and they support him.

Name ______________________________ Date ______________

from Anthony Burns: The Defeat and Triumph of a Fugitive Slave (page 750)

Active Reading SkillBuilder

Monitor

When you read, it is important to **monitor** your understanding of the material. You can do that by predicting, questioning, clarifying, connecting, evaluating and visualizing. Complete the following chart by selecting one event from the story. In the center, write the event and the page number on which it appears. Follow the strategy shown on each connecting line, and write your response in the box.

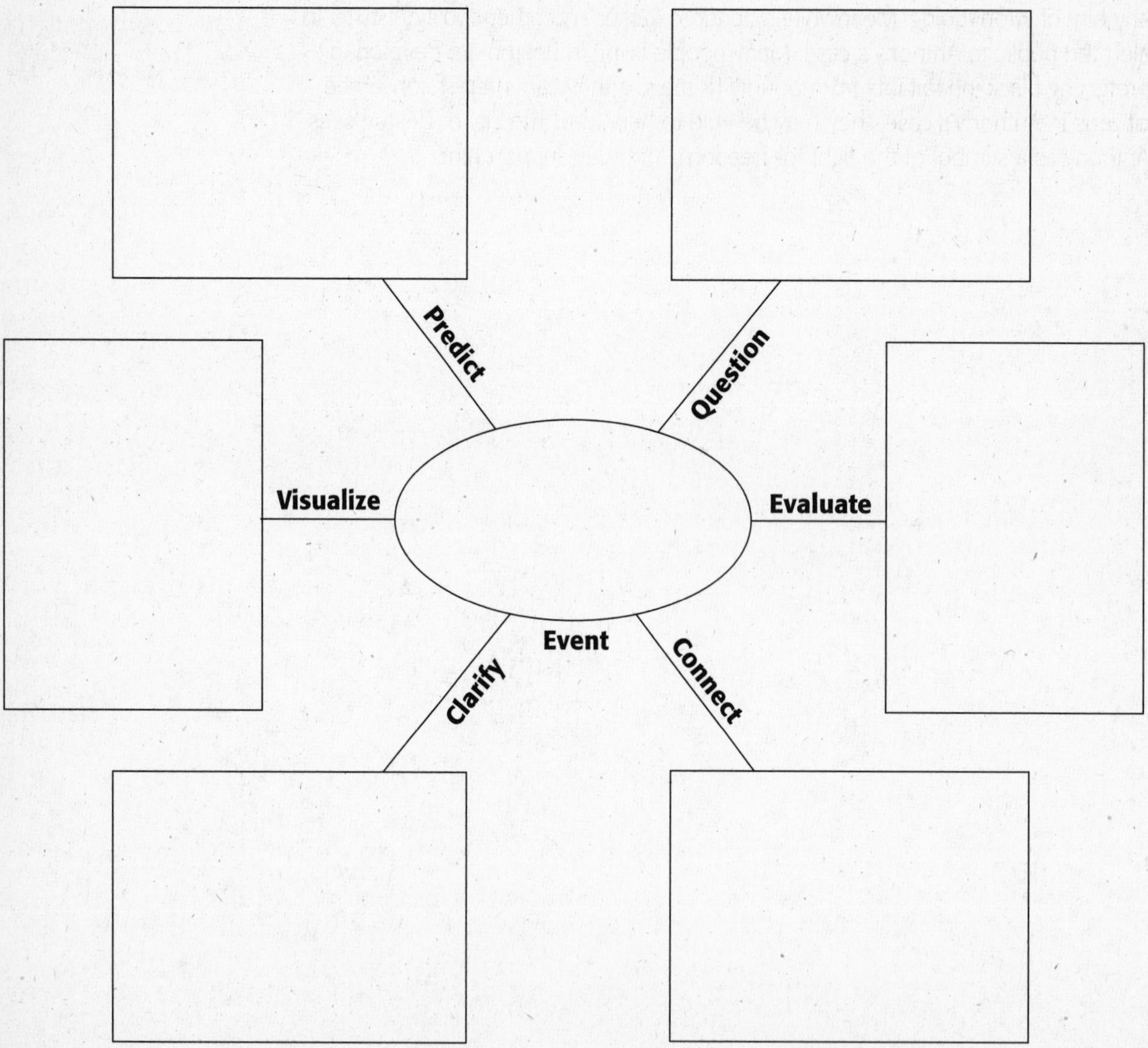

Name ______________________________ Date ______________

from Anthony Burns: The Defeat and Triumph of a Fugitive Slave (page 750)

Literary Analysis SkillBuilder

Literary Nonfiction

Literary nonfiction tells the story of a real person and/or event, but the author may fictionalize the dialogue and minor characters. Other aspects of fiction are often present as well, such as plot and conflict. Complete the chart below, listing specific literary elements from the story and how they helped you appreciate Anthony Burns's story.

Literary Element	How it Helped
Setting *The windows of the jury room were covered with iron bars like welts of pain.*	*I felt the despair and anguish Anthony felt as he sat waiting to find out his future.*
Main Character	
Other Characters	
Plot	
Conflict	
Dialogue	

Follow Up: Imagine that you read about Anthony Burns in an encyclopedia. Write a short paragraph explaining how this type of nonfiction source is different from literary nonfiction. What aspects of Burns's story might you miss out on by only reading an encyclopedia? What additional information might you gain by consulting an encyclopedia?

Name ______________________________ Date ______________

from Anthony Burns: The Defeat and Triumph of a Fugitive Slave (page 750)

Literary Analysis SkillBuilder

Conflict

A plot is usually centered around a conflict. **Conflict** occurs when a character encounters an opposing force. A conflict can be external, that is, outside the character in the form of another character, a physical obstacle, or society. A conflict can also be internal when it involves a character's struggle with him or herself. Find conflicts in the text you have read and record them in the chart. Then check whether each conflict is internal or external.

Conflict	Internal	External
Reverend Parker insists that Anthony have a lawyer, despite Anthony's fear of worsening his situation		X

Name ______________________ Date ______________

from Anthony Burns: The Defeat and Triumph of a Fugitive Slave (page 750)

Grammar SkillBuilder: Using Adjective Clauses

Key Concept: Writers use adjective clauses to help readers understand more about nouns and pronouns in their sentences.

Using Adjective Clauses

An adjective clause usually follows the noun or pronoun it modifies. It usually begins with a relative pronoun such as *who, whom, whose, that,* or *which.* Notice how the adjective clause in the sentence below gives the reader more information and makes the writing more descriptive.

Anthony Burns, **who suffered at the hands of his master,** was a gentle man.

Remember that clauses without essential information are set off with commas. Clauses starting with *that* contain essential information, while clauses starting with *which* generally do not.

Activities

A. For each sentence, supply an adjective clause to modify the italicized noun.

1. *Anthony* was alone in the city of Boston.

____

2. His *hands* were rough and callused.

____

3. The *courtroom* was dark.

____

4. *Colonel Suttle* sat watching Anthony.

____

5. The *Constitution* is the law of the land.

____

B. The following paragraph does not contain enough details. On another sheet of paper, revise it by adding more adjective clauses.

Anthony Burns thought all hope was lost. Men had come up from the South to capture him. Burns's plight was familiar to many African Americans. Abolitionists tried to help. The Fugitive Slave Act worked against them. Antislavery feelings worked for them. Anthony's fate would be decided in the courthouse.

Name ______________________________ Date ______________

from Anthony Burns: The Defeat and Triumph of a Fugitive Slave (page 750)

Words to Know SkillBuilder

Words to Know

agitate	compliance	illustrious	peer	throbbing
alleged	contradict	mobilize	petty	wretched

A. Complete each analogy with one of the Words to Know.

1. ABANDON : HOLD : : agree : ______________________
2. PROCLAIM : ANNOUNCE : : painful : ______________________
3. HANDS : GRIP : : eyes : ______________________
4. GRAVE : SERIOUS : : trivial : ______________________
5. CONQUER : RETREAT : : proven : ______________________

B. For each phrase in the first column, find the word in the second column that is closest in meaning. Write the letter of that word in the blank.

______ 1. to stare intently	A. wretched
______ 2. not for sure, supposed	B. contradict
______ 3. to stir up interest for a cause	C. alleged
______ 4. beating strongly with pain	D. petty
______ 5. of little importance	E. peer
______ 6. miserable, horrible	F. compliance
______ 7. to assemble for a purpose	G. illustrious
______ 8. the act of obeying a request	H. throbbing
______ 9. well-known	I. mobilize
______ 10. to express the opposite of	J. agitate

Name ____________________ Date ____________________

from Anthony Burns: The Defeat and Triumph of a Fugitive Slave (page 750)

Selection Quiz

Recall the characters and events in the selection. Then answer the questions in sentences or phrases.

1. Why is Anthony Burns in Boston?

2. What legal means does Colonel Suttle use to have Anthony Burns arrested in Boston? Why do Burns's captors want his arrest kept secret?

3. Why doesn't Anthony Burns want to be represented by a lawyer at first? What changes his mind?

4. Why were so many abolitionists involved in this case?

5. What important piece of legislation was passed on the first day of Burns's trial? What were the consequences of this legislation?

The People Could Fly

Retold by Virginia Hamilton

Summary

Setting: Southern United States prior to 1860

This poetic folk tale is about Africans living long ago who have the power to fly. These Africans are captured and sent across the sea to America. They must leave their wings behind. However, many of them never lose the magic power to fly. The story tells about an old man named Toby, a slave in the 1800s, who still has the magic. He works in the fields with Sarah, a woman who used to have wings. When the overseer whips Sarah and her baby, Toby uses his magic to help her find her wings. Sarah and her baby fly away to freedom. The next day, Toby speaks his magic words again, and other slaves are able to fly away, too. Toby's master wants to kill him, but Toby just laughs and flies away. Some of the slaves cannot fly, and they watch as the others fly away. They are saddened that they can't fly, yet happy that some are able to fly away to freedom. These slaves eventually escape on foot to freedom. They tell their children of the people who could fly. This story has been passed on for many generations.

Name ____________________ Date ____________________

The People Could Fly (page 767)

Active Reading SkillBuilder

Summarizing

When you tell the main ideas of a piece of writing as concisely as you can in your own words, you are **summarizing.** You condense the writer's ideas into precise statements, leaving out unimportant details. Summarize the story by answering the questions below with details from the story.

Who are the characters?

Toby, Sarah, Driver,

What is the central conflict?

What is the time and place of the story?

What are the three important events in the story?

What is the resolution of the story?

Name ________________________ Date ____________

The People Could Fly (page 767)

Literary Analysis SkillBuilder

Folk Tales

Remember that **folk tales** often combine both real and imaginary details. Imaginary details often reflect truths about real people or events. Real and fictional characters are especially important in folk tales. They can bring history alive for readers. This folk tale mentions a group of unnamed characters known only as "old and young who were called slaves," who eventually flew to freedom. Invent some names and ages for these characters. Then, based on your knowledge of the folk tale and other characters, invent one interesting detail about each of your characters. Record your ideas in the chart below.

	Name / Age	Detail
Character 1	*a young man named John, 18 years old*	*wears an angry, determined look on his face*
Character 2		
Character 3		
Character 4		

Follow Up: Record the names, ages, and details from the chart on note cards. Divide into small groups and choose one of the cards. For the character whose name you have chosen, create a story that ends with his or her meeting with Toby. Have one person in your group write the story down. Share your story by reading it to the class.

Name ____________________ Date ____________

The People Could Fly (page 767)

Active Reading SkillBuilder

Story Map

A **story map** is an outline of the setting, characters, and plot of a story. It can help you clarify what you have read or write a summary. As you read "The People Could Fly," record the major characters, the conflict, the setting, and important events in the outline below.

Title:	
Characters:	
Conflict:	
Setting:	
Event 1:	
Event 2:	
Event 3:	
Event 4:	
Event 5:	
Climax:	**Resolution:**

Name ______________________________ Date ______________

The People Could Fly (page 773)

Grammar SkillBuilder: Punctuating Dialogue

Key Concept: Writers use properly punctuated dialogue to make their writing lively and clear.

Punctuating Dialogue

Punctuating dialogue helps readers to know when and how a character speaks in a piece of writing. Use quotation marks to set off quotations. Start a new paragraph each time a new character speaks. Place periods and commas inside quotation marks. Place question marks and exclamation points inside if they are part of a quotation, outside if they are not. Capitalize the first word of a quotation that is a complete sentence.

Activity

For each situation below, write a sentence or two with correctly punctuated dialogue.

Example: The overseer yells at an exhausted Sarah to keep working.
"Hey, you!" the overseer screamed in Sarah's direction. "Get back to work!"
"Will this ever end?" wondered Sarah.

1. Sarah pleads with Toby to use the magic. ______________________________

2. Sarah tries to get her baby to be quiet. ______________________________

3. The slaves talk that night of Sarah's flight. ______________________________

4. The overseer and master plot their revenge on Toby. ______________________________

5. The slaves left on the ground discuss what they've seen. ______________________________

Name ______________________ Date ______________

The People Could Fly (page 767)

Words to Know SkillBuilder

Words to Know

glinty scorned seize shuffle snag

A. For each phrase in the first column, find the phrase in the second column that is closest in meaning. Write the letter of that phrase in the blank.

______	1. snag a trout	A. sparkling in the mist
______	2. hated and scorned	B. start sliding your feet
______	3. glinty with dew	C. detested and shunned
______	4. seize the moment	D. catch a fish
______	5. begin to shuffle	E. hold on to now

B. Cross out the italicized word or phrase. Above it, write the Word to Know that could replace it.

1. Sharp twisted branches seemed to *clutch and tear at* her face and hair as she ran through the woods.
2. He tried to *grasp roughly* the old man, but he slipped easily away from him.
3. The people did not *drag their feet on the ground;* they began to fly in the air as if they were birds or angels.
4. They were *treated with hostility and disrespect,* despite the fact that they worked so hard.
5. Several *shimmering* pieces of black coal were embedded in the dirt.

C. Create a diary entry that Sarah might write upon becoming free. Use all the Words to Know in your entry.

Name ______________________ Date ______________

The People Could Fly (page 767)

Selection Quiz

Recall the characters and events in the selection. Then answer the questions in sentences or phrases.

1. Who are Toby and Sarah?

2. Why is Sarah suffering so terribly at the beginning of the story? What does her suffering cause her to forget?

3. How does Sarah regain her ability to fly? What is the reaction of the Overseer?

4. What do the Overseer, the Driver, and the Master mean to do to Toby? How does Toby respond?

5. Why do the people who cannot fly tell the story to their children? What does this do for them?

Writing Workshop

Research Report

Prewriting

One way to find a focus for your research report is to choose a topic that interests you and then brainstorm different aspects of it. Write a main topic in the center circle of the cluster diagram below. Then write ideas related to the topic in the connecting circles. In the outer circles, write ideas related to the first ones. When you have completed the diagram, choose an idea for your research paper.

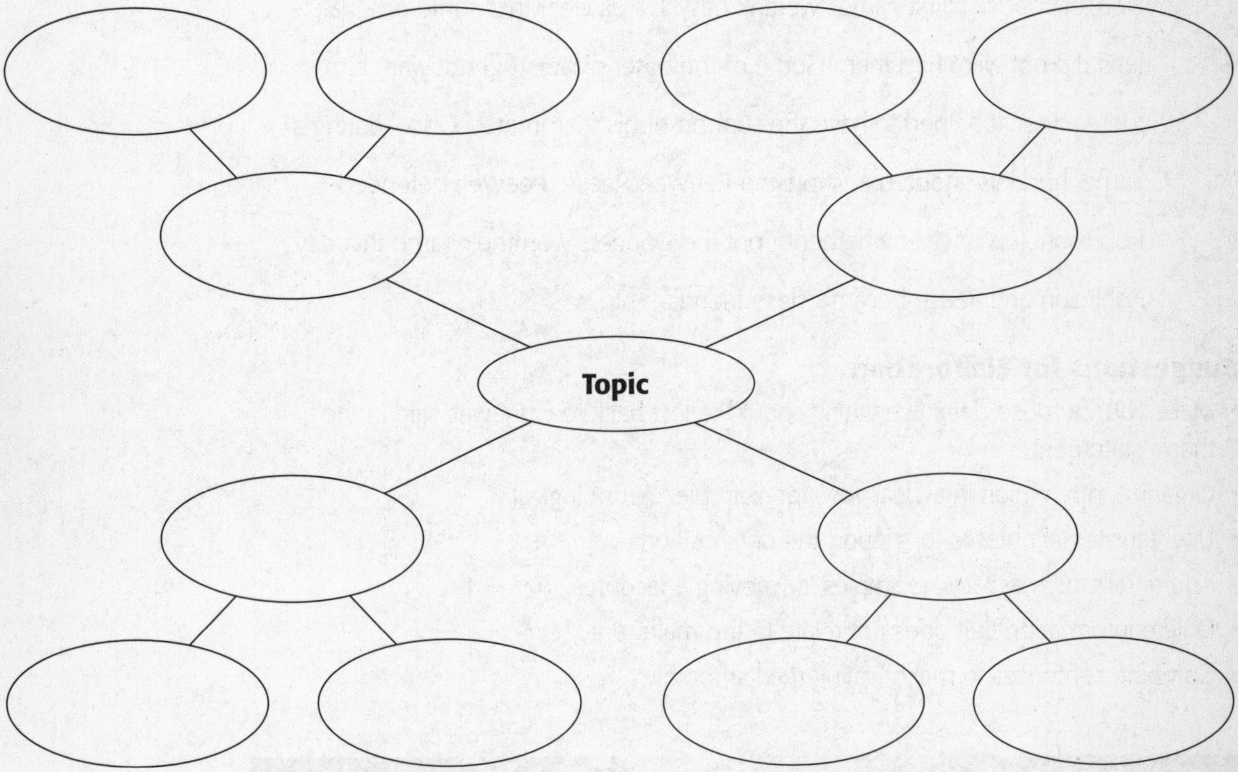

Once you have explored your topic and decided how to focus your paper, you should write out your report's purpose in a complete sentence. This sentence is called your thesis statement. Be sure that it clearly states your topic.

Topic: ______________________________

Purpose: ______________________________

Thesis statement: ______________________________

____

Research Report

Drafting and Elaboration

The paragraph below is from the first draft of the body of a student's research report. It does not connect the information to the thesis and it does not have enough specific details. Make connections clear by following the Suggestions for Elaboration. You can use information from your Reader's Notebook or add your own ideas. Write your paragraph on a separate sheet of paper.

Draft

Branch Rickey officially announced Robinson's place on the Brooklyn Dodgers. Jackie's first games weren't easy. It was clear that some baseball fans did not want him there. Some of the other players did not want him there either. It helped to have the support of his teammates. Once, during a game, hecklers shouted at shortstop PeeWee Reese. PeeWee defended Robinson. It is unclear whether or not the Dodgers won their game that day. Robinson and Reese became close friends.

Suggestions for Elaboration

- Make your purpose clear. Everything should reflect back to what was said in the thesis statement.
- Organize information in a clear way, for example, chronologically.
- Use transitional phrases to support the organization.
- Add details such as facts, examples, or moving anecdotes.
- Delete information that does not relate to the main topic.
- Combine sentences to make writing read smoothly.

Reader's Notebook

Branch Rickey announced Robinson's place on the Brooklyn Dodgers. ■ His announcement was historic. ■ Jackie Robinson played his first games with the Dodgers in the Spring of 1947. ■ Fans jeered and other baseball players made threats. ■ Hecklers asked how PeeWee could play baseball with a black man. ■ They were playing a game against the Boston Braves. ■ PeeWee stood beside Jackie and put his arm around him. ■ PeeWee's action silenced the crowd.

Research Report

Peer Response Guide

Because you are doing a research report, your purpose is to inform your readers. You must try to include just the right amount of meaningful information, and you must present this information in a way that is clear and focused. To make sure that your essay is informative, clear, and focused, ask a peer reviewer to read it and answer the following questions.

1. What is my thesis statement? Do I need to develop it further? How could it be stated more clearly?

   Response:

   Suggestions for Revision:

2. Do I stay focused on my thesis statement? How could I more fully develop my ideas in the report?

   Response:

   Suggestions for Revision:

3. Are the primary and secondary sources I have cited helpful? Do they support my ideas?

   Response:

   Suggestions for Revision:

Peer Response Guide continued

4. What other information or background would you like to know about to help you understand my report?

   Response:

   Suggestions for Revision:

5. What specific details, facts, and examples help support my thesis the most? Is there any information that does not support my thesis, that does not need to be in the report?

   Response:

   Suggestions for Revision:

6. Do I reach a satisfying conclusion? How could I improve the final paragraph?

   Response:

   Suggestions for Revision:

Research Report

Revising, Editing, and Proofreading

Revising

TARGET SKILL ▶ Presenting Ideas in a Logical Order

As you revise your research report, ask yourself the following questions:

- Have I chosen the most logical order for my ideas?
- Have I been consistent in following that order?
- Have I made my ideas clear to my reader?
- Have I helped my reader by using transitional phrases?
- Have I included enough background information in my report?

Editing and Proofreading

TARGET SKILL ▶ Clauses as Fragments

Use the suggestions given below to revise and proofread the following paragraph from the rough draft of one student's research report. Then correct errors in grammar, usage, mechanics, and spelling using proofreading marks. Finally, copy your corrected draft onto a separate sheet of paper.

- Be sure that all sentences are complete.
- Connect subordinating clauses to another sentence with a comma.
- Combine sentences so that the information flows smoothly.
- Use the correct conjunction to connect ideas.

Draft

This was a long time ago, but things were very different back then. Today we have many sports heroes. We worship them. But in 1945 blacks did not play on white teams. One man wanted this to end, however. The president of the Brooklyn Dodgers, Branch Rickey. Wanted to integrate his team. After doing some talent scouting. Because he chose Jackie Robinson. Jackie Robinson became a hero. Although it was courageous and hard for Jackie to do so. A lot of people felt threatened by this. Because they didn't accept it easily. That Jackie was playing with the Dodgers.

Applying

Now edit and proofread your own research report. Refer to the bulleted list above.

Research Report

Strong Student Model

Jackie Robinson: Not Just a Baseball Hero

1. Introduction leads into the report and provides a thesis statement, showing the author's intent.

Another Option:
• Start with a short anecdote to draw the reader's interest.

All he really wanted to do was play baseball. Although the great Jackie Robinson didn't exactly set out to become a civil rights hero, as the first African American to play professional baseball in the National League, that is exactly what he became. This essay will show why he is a hero.

2. Gives historical background from different sources

In 1945, the country was divided by racism. Blacks and whites played baseball in separate leagues. Branch Rickey, the president of the Brooklyn Dodgers, wanted to find a good ball player who could be the first black man in professional baseball in the United States. He chose Jackie Robinson, an all-around athlete who had served in the military and was playing on an all-black baseball team. Rickey knew Robinson would need courage to play in the face of ugly racial abuse. He asked Jackie if he had the guts to look away when people insulted him. Jackie responded, "Mr. Rickey, are you looking for a Negro who is afraid to fight back?"

3. Provides an anecdote with quotes that gives historical background

"No," Branch Rickey said. "I'm looking for a ballplayer with guts enough not to fight back." (Adler 30)

4. Organizes ideas in paragraphs, and lists events in chronological order

On April 10, 1947, Branch Rickey officially announced Robinson's place on the Brooklyn Dodgers. It was an historic day. However, Jackie's first games in the Spring of 1947 weren't easy. He ignored jeering fans and members of the other teams who threatened him during games. It helped to have the support of his teammates. Once, during a game against the Braves in Boston, hecklers shouted at shortstop PeeWee Reese, asking how he could play on the same team as a black man. PeeWee did not answer with words. Instead he went over, stood beside Jackie, and put his arm around him. That action silenced the crowd. (Scott 47–48)

5. Provides an anecdote that shows historical significance of thesis

6. The conclusion summarizes Robinson's great achievements and the role he played in history.

Jackie played with the Dodgers from 1947 to1956. Because of his example, many other black men joined the major leagues. He was an accomplished baseball player who helped his team to win the World Series in 1955. (Adler 38–41) His greatest achievement, however, was breaking the color barrier in baseball.

Works Cited

7. Includes a correctly formatted Works Cited list

Scott, Richard. Jackie Robinson. Broomall, PA: Chelsea House Publishers, 1987.

Adler, David A. Jackie Robinson: He Was the First. New York: Holiday House, 1989.

Research Report

Average Student Model

Jackie Robinson, Baseball Hero

1. The introduction states a fact, which is not enough for a thesis statement. Develop the thesis statement so that it reflects the purpose of the whole essay.

Jackie Robinson was a very good athlete, especially in baseball. He was signed up to play with the Brooklyn Dodgers in 1947. That wasn't the main thing he accomplished, however. Jackie Robinson was the first African American to play baseball in the National League.

In 1945 he was playing baseball with an all-black team. Because in 1945 blacks did not play on white teams. The president of the Brooklyn Dodgers, Branch Rickey, wanted a black player on his team. After doing some talent scouting, he chose Jackie Robinson. (Adler 28)

2. The order of the facts is not logical. Events should be given in chronological order.

This was hard for some white people to take, hard for them to understand. And they gave Jackie a lot of racial abuse. Branch Rickey wanted Jackie to be able to take it without fighting back, and so he did. He never responded to insults from the crowds or other players.

April 10, 1947 was an historic day. That's when it was announced to the papers that Jackie would play with the Dodgers.

3. It is not clear how this background information is relevant.

Another Option:
• Use transitional phrases to make connections.

In college, at UCLA, he not only played baseball, but football, basketball, and track. He was an all-around athlete. He also served in the US Army. He got married and he and his wife had a son, Jackie Jr. But now, at age 28, he was playing professional baseball.

4. This anecdote is incomplete; details are left out that would make the report more interesting.

Throughout the years he played with the Dodgers, Jackie had the support of his own teammates. They got to know him and saw what a good man he was. They stood by him, no matter what. One shortstop put his arm around Jackie during a game, showing the crowd that they were friends. (Scott 47–48)

5. The information in the conclusion is valuable, but the main point is not clearly summarized.

Jackie played with the Dodgers from 1947 to 1956. During his years of playing baseball, many other black men joined the major leagues. In 1955 the Dodgers won the World Series they finally won and were the world champions of baseball. This was the greatest thrill of Jackie's life. (Adler 38–41)

Works Cited

6. Includes a correctly formatted Works Cited list

Scott, Richard. Jackie Robinson. Broomall, PA: Chelsea House Publishers, 1987.

Adler, David A. Jackie Robinson: He Was the First. New York: Holiday House, 1989.

Research Report

Weak Student Model

Jackie Robinson: A Portrait

1. Thesis statement is vague. Make sure thesis statement states the purpose of the essay.

Jackie Robinson was a very good athlete, especially in baseball. He was signed up to play with the Brooklyn Dodgers in 1947. Although the great Jackie Robinson didn't exactly set out to do so, he became more than just a baseball hero.

This was a long time ago, and things were very different back then. Today we have many African American sports heroes. We worship them. But in 1945 blacks did not play on white teams. One man wanted this to end, however. The president of the Brooklyn Dodgers, Branch Rickey. He wanted to integrate his team. After doing some talent scouting. He chose Jackie Robinson. He made Jackie Robinson a hero.

2. This paragraph includes sentence fragments. Attach modifying clauses to the sentence they modify.

3. Writer should use specific examples, supporting research with facts, details, and/or anecdotes.

Although it was courageous and hard for Jackie to do so. A lot of people felt threatened by this. They didn't accept it easily, that Jackie was playing with the Dodgers. Jackie was very strong. He didn't fight back. Rickey told him not to. He told him to have the courage not to fight back.

4. The information is vague; sources are not cited.

Throughout the years he played with the Dodgers, Jackie had the support of his own teammates. They got to know him, and saw what a good man he was. They stood by him, no matter what. One shortstop put his arm around Jackie during a game, showing the crowds that they were friends. His wife supported him. Black fans really supported him a lot. Black people had not come to baseball games before. But now they had a hero. They came to see Jackie play.

5. The conclusion lists Jackie's accomplishments but does not make clear what the main point is.

Jackie played with the Dodgers for nine years. He was a great baseball player. One year the Dodgers won the World Series. To me, that is what makes a baseball player truly great.

Works Cited

Scott, Richard Jackie Robinson. Chelsea House Publishers, 1987

Adler, David A. Jackie Robinson: He Was the First. New York: Holiday House, 1989

6. Includes a Works Cited list, but the entries are not formatted correctly

Research Report

Rubric for Evaluation

Ideas and Content	Weak	Average	Strong
1. Thesis statement clearly states the topic and purpose			
2. Information presented supports the main topic; report has focus			
3. Uses enough evidence from primary and secondary sources to develop thesis			
4. Presents new ideas clearly			
5. Conclusion is strong and summarizes thesis			

Structure and Form			
6. Information is well-organized and clear			
7. Transitions between ideas are strong			

Grammar, Usage, and Mechanics			
8. Uses correct grammar			
9. Uses correct punctuation, capitalization, and spelling			

Writing Progress to Date (Writing Portfolio)

The strongest aspect of this writing is ______________________________

____

The final version shows improvement over the rough draft in this way: ______________________________

____

____

A specific improvement over past assignments in your portfolio is ______________________________

____

A skill to work on in future assignments is ______________________________

Additional comments: ______________________________

____

Reviewing Literary Concepts (page 789)

Reflect and Assess

OPTION 1 **Historical Fiction and Literary Nonfiction**

Historical Fiction		Literary Nonfiction	
Strengths	**Weaknesses**	**Strengths**	**Weaknesses**

Answer Key
Unit Five

from Exploring the *Titanic*

Active Reading SkillBuilder, page 5

Responses will vary. Possible responses are provided.

Facts

- On May 21, 1911, the hull of the Titanic was launched. (page 660)
- Captain Edward J. Smith was given command. (page 661)
- The captain ordered the lookouts to keep a sharp watch for ice. (page 665)
- The ship had received seven warnings of icebergs the day it sank. (page 665)

Unsupported Opinions

- The captain was a natural leader and popular. (page 661)
- The ship moved majestically down the River Test. (page 664)
- Mrs. Thayer couldn't help feeling that something was very wrong. (page 666)
- The night air was biting cold. (page 668)

Opinions Supported with Facts

- The dining room was beautiful. (page 662)
- Phillips was annoyed by the Californian's message. (page 665)
- Twenty minutes after the crash, things looked very bad. (page 666)
- Captain Smith was a very worried man. (page 668)

Literary Analysis SkillBuilder, page 6

Responses will vary. Possible responses are provided.

Description: p. 663 "The Titanic was rather like a big floating layer cake."
Secondary source: p. 663 Graphic shows the layers of decks and floors.

Description: p. 670 "Out on the decks, most passengers now began to move toward the stern area, which was slowly lifting out of the water."
Secondary Source: p. 669 Painting depicts the stern of the boat in the air.

Description: p. 671 "Before long this ghastly wail stopped, as the freezing water took its toll."
Primary Source: p. 671 Newspaper reinforces the idea of the freezing water taking its toll.

Literary Analysis SkillBuilder, page 7

Responses will vary. Possible responses are provided.

Source: Eyewitness description by Ruth of the loading of the lifeboats. p. 668
Accurate?: Yes, her account probably would correspond to the memories of other Titanic survivors.
Reliable?: Eyewitness accounts are generally reliable, but a person may exaggerate or be mistaken about specific details.

Source: Photograph of grand staircase, page 661
Accurate?: Yes, the staircase of the Titanic looked as it did in the picture.
Reliable?: In general, photographs are reliable records of what something looked like. However, the way the photograph is taken can affect the viewer's impression of the subject.

Source: Newspaper, page 671
Accurate?: Yes, the facts in the newspaper are probably accurate. You could check by looking at other accounts of the events and of the number of lives lost.
Reliable?: Newspapers are generally reliable. They try to get their information from official sources and check their facts. Sometimes new information will be discovered after the newspaper is printed, so it is a good idea to compare early information from a newspaper the day of the event with final information.

Grammar SkillBuilder, page 8

A.
1. The *Titanic* was eleven stories high, and it had the biggest whistles in the world.
2. First-class passengers had the best of everything, but third-class passengers were crowded into compartments in the bottom of the ship.
3. Passengers wanting exercise could swim in the pool, or they could use the rowing machines.
4. Harold Bride was the assistant wireless operator, and he was pleased with his new job.
5. On Sunday, passengers might nap on deck, or they might visit with friends.

B.
1. *Caronia* sent
2. Harold Bride took, it was received; compound
3. Jack Thayer walked
4. lookout spotted, he told; compound
5. They tried, they turned; compound

C. Accept responses that accurately use at least **three** of the Words to Know.

Words to Know SkillBuilder, page 9

A.
1. feverishly
2. dazzled
3. indefinitely
4. eerie
5. novelty

from **Exploring the *Titanic*,** *continued*

The boxed letters spell out *safety.*

B. 1. B
2. D
3. E
4. A
5. C

C. Accept responses that accurately use at least **three** Words to Know.

Selection Quiz, page 10

Responses will vary. Possible responses are provided.

1. Four compartments could fill with water and the ship would still float. Also there was a mechanical device to close compartment doors and seal them off.
2. The story about the *Titan,* the eyewitness who described *Titanic's* size as "nightmarish," and the problem of another ship breaking away from its mooring when the *Titanic* was departing all foreshadow the disaster.
3. People—possibly including the captain—believed the ship to be unsinkable; the crew had not seen any icebergs themselves; initial iceberg warnings were ignored; the radio operators were kept too busy with personal messages to pay proper attention to later warnings; on a quiet sea, it is harder to spot icebergs.
4. All these contributed to the loss of life: Insufficient lifeboats; the nearest ship had turned off its radio; no other ship was near enough to get there before the *Titanic* sank; the cold temperature of the water meant that people could not survive long.
5. It was on such a huge scale, it involved important people, and it was very dramatic and unexpected.

The Lives of *La Belle*

Active Reading SkillBuilder, page 11

Cause: La Belle ran aground on March 15.
Effect/Cause: Colony's supplies and trade goods are lost.
Effect/Cause: La Salle realizes he is cut off from France and his dream colony is doomed.
Effect/Cause: La Salle continues to search for the Mississippi.
Effect: He never finds it.

Active Reading SkillBuilder, page 12

Responses will vary. Possible responses are provided.
***The Lives of* La Belle:** Map, section title, subheadings
Both: Title, byline, photos and captions, important idea is placed in a special box
***Exploring the* Titanic:** Cutaway illustration, artist's renderings of event

Last Cover

Active Reading SkillBuilder, page 14

Responses will vary. Possible responses are provided.
Details from the Story: "It goes back to a winter afternoon after I'd hunted the woods. . . . I had walked, reading signs, looking for a delicate print in the damp soil."
How I Picture Them: The ground is muddy, not snowy. The trees are bare and the air is raw.

Details from the Story: "It was late February, and I remember the bleak, dead cold that had set in, cold that was a rare thing for our Carolina hills."
How I Picture Them: It is very quiet and the colors of the woods are subtle: brown, gray, black, and white. Nothing is moving.

Details from the Story: "I remember the day well, the racing clouds, the wind rattling the tops of the pine trees and swaying the Spanish moss."
How I Picture Them: It is a beautiful spring day with blue sky, fluffy clouds, and gusts of wind.

Details from the Story: "His knowing, crafty mask blended perfectly with the shadows and a mass of drift and branches that had collected by the bank of the pool."
How I Picture Them: There is dappled sunlight casting shadows, branches and leaves float on the smooth surface of the pool, and two bright eyes peer out of the darkness.

Literary Analysis SkillBuilder, page 15

Responses will vary. Possible responses are provided.
Place description: "A week later the woods were budding, and the thickets were rustling with all manner of wild things scurrying on the love scent."
Where it fits: The boys have just found Bandit's den and have agreed not to tell their father.
Drama: It conveys the excitement of spring and adds reality to what Bandit's life is like now.
Place description: ". . . stood listening for a time by the deep, shaded pool where for years we boys had gone swimming, sailed boats, and dreamed summer dreams. . . . It was Bandit, craftily submerged there, all but his head resting in the cool water of the pool and the shadow of the two big beeches that spread above it. . . . His knowing, crafty mask blended perfectly with the shadows and a mass of drift and branches that had collected by the bank of the pool."
Where it fits: The hunt is on for Bandit. He has been eluding the hunters.

Drama: The reader now knows something the hunters don't and is drawn into the story further.

Follow Up: Responses will depend on descriptive passages chosen.

Literary Analysis SkillBuilder, page 16

Responses will vary. Possible responses are provided.

Colin

Trait: Sensitive
Evidence: Worried and upset about losing the fox.
Trait: Quiet
Evidence: He spends a lot of time thinking about the fox, walking in the woods and drawing. He doesn't argue loudly with his father over the fox.
Trait: Artistic
Evidence: He draws very well
Trait: Stubborn
Evidence: He refuses to give up the fox and tracks him all summer.

Father

Trait: Practical
Evidence: He sees Colin's art as frivolous; he insists the fox be returned to the woods because he is a nuisance to farmers.
Trait: Respects nature
Evidence: He is full of lore about the woods; he sees hunting as a way to connect to nature; he refuses to participate in the unfair fox hunt.
Trait: Open to new ideas
Evidence: By the end, he has accepted Colin's art and sees it as another way of showing the same love for nature that he feels.
Trait: Serious
Evidence: He chooses his words and doesn't speak frivolously; he makes judgments carefully.

Follow Up: Both share a deep love of nature, a determination to do what they believe is right, and an artistic or poetic nature, which Colin shows in his art and the father in his store of poetry and lore and his eventual appreciation of Colin's drawing. Both are reserved, as well. The reserve and stubbornness are obstacles at first to their developing a relationship, but eventually their similarities lead them to a deeper understanding and respect for each other.

Grammar SkillBuilder, page 17

A.
1. After the fox made away with his first young chicken, Father suggested we name him Bandit.
2. It's always a sad time in the woods when the seven sleepers are under cover.
3. The boys meant a lot to Bandit while he was a kit.
4. Ever since I was ten, I'd been allowed to hunt with Father.
5. When he gets through with his spring sparking, he may come back.

B. *Responses will vary. Possible responses are provided.*
1. As summer came on, Bandit began to live up to Father's predictions.
2. The dogs chased the wrong fox for twenty minutes before they realized their mistake.
3. The short day was nearing an end when I heard the horn sound again.
4. Bandit's secret had been Colin's since an afternoon three months before when he'd watched the fox swim downstream to hide in the deep pool.
5. Father sat holding the picture with a sort of tenderness for a long time while we glowed in the warmth of the shared secret.

Words to Know SkillBuilder, page 18

A.
1. essence
2. harried
3. sanctuary
4. bleak
5. invalid
6. confound
7. predestined
8. passive
9. wily
10. sanction

B. Accept responses that accurately use at least **five** Words to Know.

Selection Quiz, page 19

Responses will vary. Possible responses are provided.
1. The father and another hunter kill the fox's mother, so it will die if left on its own. Colin is so upset that their mother, worried about him, also wants to raise the kit.
2. They both have a strong love for and understanding of nature. The father is a hunter and tracker—someone who does things. Colin is an observer and artist—someone who creates things.
3. He understands that it must be done, but he dislikes the way it is being carried out. He disapproves of dispensing with the rules of fox-hunting.
4. He loves him, and worries about him. They exchange a glance that tells Stan everything about his brother. He will always carry that understanding with him.
5. He realizes it when Colin draws the picture of Bandit's last hiding place. He sees that his son has a great understanding and appreciation of the woods and its creatures. He respects Colin's observational and drawing abilities and realizes how important a role Colin can play.

Building Vocabulary SkillBuilder

page 20

Responses will vary. Possible responses are provided.

1. shocks
2. one level of a building
3. smile broadly
4. intelligently sharp
5. illuminated
6. edge
7. a section of a building
8. students who meet to study the same subject
9. a usually rectangular section of a town or city bounded on each side by streets
10. have an influence

A Crown of Wild Olive

Active Reading SkillBuilder, page 31

Responses will vary. Possible responses are provided.

Cause: Amyntas runs fast.
Effect: He gets chosen to represent Athens in a race. (becomes Cause)
Effect: He travels to the race site and meets Leon. (becomes Cause)
Effect: They become friends.

Cause: Leon hurts his foot.
Effect: Amyntas thinks about winning the race unfairly. (becomes Cause)
Effect: Amyntas leaves an offering for Zeus and prays to run a good race and do nothing else. (becomes Cause)
Effect: He runs the best race he can, and wins.

Literary Analysis SkillBuilder, page 32

Responses will vary. Possible responses are provided.

Historical Details

Every fourth summer a general truce was declared so all Greek city-states could participate in the Olympic Games.
A herald visited each Greek city-state with the news of the Olympic truce.
A statue of Athene, goddess of wisdom, stood in the Citadel of Athens.
Games were held in a valley near the sanctuary of Zeus at Olympia.
Athletes practiced for a month at Olympia in preparation for the games.
A crown of wild olive was the prize given a victor in any event.
Spartan boys were beaten to toughen them and teach them to resist pain.
Olympic events included racing, javelin and discus throwing, and wrestling.
Spartans disliked money and had no coinage.
Spartan boys were allowed to have only one tunic at a time.
The wild olive trees from which victor's crowns were made grew around the temple of Zeus.
The only women allowed at the games were the Priestesses of Demeter.

Imaginative Details

Amyntas felt lonely among all the older contestants.
Amyntas promised his father that he would run his best and win for them both.
On the first day, Amyntas was so nervous he thought the food had no more flavor than food eaten in a dream.
Contestants grumbled about having to clean four years' growth of weeds from the stadium.
Leon disliked the fair because he had no money to spend.
Amyntas thought that if Leon were out of the race because of his injury, Amyntas would surely win.
Amyntas bought a small bronze bull and a knife at the fair.
Amyntas offered the bull to Zeus as a sign of gratitude.

Follow Up: Students may generalize that Spartan upbringing was harsher than Athenian. Spartans seemed to value toughness and getting along without many material comforts. Athenians seemed to value poetry, art, and philosophy.

Literary Analysis SkillBuilder, page 33

Responses will vary. Possible responses are provided.

Setting

- "Soon the crowd on shore was only a shingle of dark and colored and white along the waterfront."
- ". . . the first dappled fingers of sunlight shafting in the doorway of his cell."

Characters

- ". . . and somewhat self-conscious that he had not yet sacrificed his boy's long hair to Apollo."
- "from shoulder to flank [his back] was criss-crossed with scars, past the purple stage but not yet faded to the silvery white they would be in a few year's time; pinkish scars that looked as though the skin were still drawn uncomfortably tight over them."
- "His belly was churning now, his heart banging away right up in his throat so that it almost choked him."

Events

- "Aboard the Paralos, all was the ordered bustle of departure, ropes being cast off, rowers in their places at the oars."
- "He came up for air, spluttering and shaking the water out of his eyes."
- "He ducked his head to the place, sucked hard and spat crimson into the water."

A Crown of Wild Olive, *continued*

Grammar SkillBuilder, page 34

A.
1. Amyntas waved farewell to his father, who had also been a runner.
2. The port that was the closest to Olympia was five days distance from Athens.
3. The journey, which was his first, finally ended.
4. Early on, Amyntas met Leon, who was about the same age as he.
5. They walked among the booths, which had sprung up recently.

B. *Responses will vary. Possible responses are provided.*
1. Leon cut his foot on something that was lying half-buried.
2. Amyntas, whose concern was for his friend, cleaned and bound the foot.
3. The runners that were assembled came from near and far.
4. The stadium, which was in Olympia, was filled with spectators.
5. The race, which was close, ended with Amyntas emerging as the winner.

Words to Know SkillBuilder, page 35

A.
1. angular
2. reel
3. dappled
4. substance
5. unaccountably

B.
1. synonyms
2. antonyms
3. synonyms
4. antonyms
5. synonyms

C. Accept responses that accurately use at least **three** Words to Know.

Selection Quiz, page 36

Responses will vary. Possible responses are provided.
1. They have been held for more than 300 years. There is a truce throughout the entire region.
2. He promises to run the best race that is in him and, if the gods allow, to win for them both. Ariston, Amyntas's father, can no longer run because of an injury to his knee received in a war with Sparta.
3. He makes an offering to Zeus and prays to run his best race and nothing more. He may feel that he needs extra help to keep to his path.
4. He would like Leon to have the pleasure of winning. He decides it would be an insult to Leon to let him win.
5. He hopes that they will never meet again. Should they meet, it would be as enemies and one might have to kill the other.

Passing on the Flame

Active Reading SkillBuilder, page 37

Responses will vary. Possible responses are provided.

The purpose of both articles is to inform.
1. The Web article uses a title, photographs, and captions.
2. You could read the title and the captions and look at the pictures to get an idea of what the article will be about. Because the article does not have subheadings, you could skim a few paragraphs see what information will be covered.
3. The textbook article uses a title, subheads, an objectives statement, photographs, captions, pulled-out text, key terms, and a map and legend.
4. The objectives statement, title, subheadings and pull quotes would help me remember the content of the article. Key words would help me review important vocabulary, and the map would let me visually review important information.
5. Both have titles, photographs, and captions. A title helps readers know what the article will be about. The photographs add interest to the article, and the captions allow readers to understand what the photograph is showing.
6. Organizers such as titles, subheadings and pulled text are fairly generic and can be used with articles of varying content. Other organizers such as photographs and maps depend more on the type of information in the article. For example, the Web article describes modern events, so photographs are possible. The textbook article deals with ancient history, so the only photographs available are modern photographs of objects such as the statue pictured that have survived the centuries. The textbook article focuses on the Roman Empire and includes a map of the region. The Web article does not concentrate on one geographic location, so a map would not be very useful.
7. Some students may say the textbook article's many organizers helped them understand and stay interested in the complex information. Other students may find the organizers distracting and prefer the straightforward approach of the Web article.

Active Reading SkillBuilder, page 38

Responses will vary. Possible responses are provided.
Topic: The Olympic torch

Predict: Countries try to have a meaningful torch lighting ceremony. Possibly at the next Olympic Games, they will tell the story of the host country's native people.

Connect: They carried the torch through my town for the 1996 Olympics.

Question: What were the two ancient symbols that Carl Diem combined to create the torch relay?

Clarify: The tradition of the relay began with the Greeks. The Greek cities were often at war. To let participants travel to the Games safely, the Greeks sent runners throughout the land to announce there was a truce so the Olympics could take place.

Visualize: Jesse Owens' third jump, where he uses his own mark and leaps to victory.

Evaluate: The tradition of peace during the Greek Olympics sounds better than modern nations' tradition of choosing not to attend Olympics when they are hosted by an enemy.

from Long Walk to Freedom

Active Reading SkillBuilder, page 40

Responses will vary. Possible responses are provided.

Main Idea

Mandela believes that if people can be taught to hate, they can also be taught to love.

Supporting Details

He knows that deep in every human heart is mercy and generosity.
No one is born hating others.
Love comes more naturally than hate.
He could always see humanity in the prison guards.

Literary Analysis SkillBuilder, page 41

Responses will vary. Possible responses are provided.

Experiences in Mandela's Life

As a child, Mandela likes to swim and roast mealies under the stars.
He lives as a young man in Johannesburg.
Mandela joins the African National Congress.
Mandela experiences hardships in prison.
He walks out of prison.

What He Learned from Them

Looking back, he realizes that he was truly born free.
He sees that his people are not free to live full lives.
He sees that people pay a high price to fight for what they believe in. He is not willing to enjoy advantages others can't share.
He learns that even in the guards he can still see a "glimmer of humanity." He sees that neither oppressor nor oppressed is free.
He learns that real freedom is not just being free oneself, but respecting and enhancing the freedom of others as well.

Follow Up: A biography is usually told in the third person, by a narrator who was not a witness to the events he or she describes. The author of a biography must piece together the story from research and interviews with many people. A memoir is first-person, told by the person who actually lived the events. If this had been a biography, readers would learn more about Mandela's actions and less about how he feels and what he learned as the result of those actions.

Active Reading SkillBuilder, page 42

Statement: "The policy of apartheid created a deep and lasting wound in my country and my people."
Shows: Mandela is opposed to the policy and believes it has deeply hurt South Africa.

Statement: "I never lost hope that this great transformation would occur."
Shows: Mandela believes that the old system of apartheid had to change.

Statement: "My commitment to my people . . . was at the expense of the people I knew best and loved most."
Shows: Mandela struggled with his obligations to be a leader and to be with his family. He regrets that he could not be a better parent and husband, and blames the system for making him choose.

Statement: "It was this desire for the freedom of my people . . . that drove a law-abiding attorney to become a criminal."
Shows: Mandela believes it is acceptable to break unjust laws for an important cause.

Statement: "My hunger for freedom became a hunger for the freedom of all people, white and black."
Shows: Mandela believes achieving equality between blacks and whites will be good for both sides.

Statement: "My long walk is not yet ended."
Shows: He believes the country still needs more change.

Grammar SkillBuilder, page 43

A.
1. , which I loved,
2. who had restrictions on his activities
3. who looked like I did
4. , which fought to abolish apartheid
5. , which had been somewhat ordinary,

B. *Responses will vary. Possible responses are provided.*
1. In my absence, which lasted for decades, my family suffered.

Passing on the Flame, *continued*

2. There were guards in prison who showed some humanity.
3. The understanding that everyone is hurt by racism came to me in prison.
4. I have never stopped believing in the idea that all people will one day be free.
5. I know that the people of South Africa, who are its true hidden treasures, will survive.

Words to Know SkillBuilder, page 44

A. 1. incomprehensible
2. indivisible
3. resiliency
4. transitory
5. curtailed

B. Accept interviews that accurately use all **five** Words to Know.

Selection Quiz, page 45

Responses will vary. Possible responses are provided.

1. He started off thinking that he was free. He learned as a young man that he was not free, nor were others who looked like him. After being imprisoned, he realized that the people doing the oppressing were not free either, and he ended with the belief that everyone needs freeing.
2. He thinks its people are its greatest resource.
3. He realized that no black person was free in South Africa, and he wanted to change that.
4. He thinks that if you are the one taking away another's freedom, you are locked behind bars of prejudice and narrow-mindedness, and not truly free.
5. They must live in a way that respects and enhances the freedom of others.

The Elephant / The Turtle

Active Reading SkillBuilder, page 46

Responses will vary. Possible responses are provided.

"The Elephant"

Main Idea: The elephant wants to remember who he was before captivity because he is unhappy. ***Important Details:*** He is sick of the rope and chain. He wants his previous strength back. He wants his life in the forest back. He wants man to disappear and to go live with the animals again.

Main Idea: The elephant dreams what it might be like to be free again. ***Important Details:*** He'll wander out at dawn, and he'll feel the wind and walk in the clear water. He will visit those he's loved before, and he'll play with his own kind.

Paraphrase: The elephant is reminiscing about his past life and wishes he could go back. He hates the rope and chain that bind him. He hates how man has made him carry heavy loads, and he feels like he has no strength left. He wants to live in the forest again, free to roam and wander where he chooses. He misses his friends and family, and he wants to renew those relationships. He wishes he had never seen man.

"The Turtle"

Main Idea: The turtle's life is part of nature's life cycle even though she doesn't understand it. ***Important Details:*** She was born to do this thing. She doesn't even consider it. It came to her from out of nature. It's as much a part of her life as walking.

Main Idea: The turtle has an important part in the chain of life. ***Important Details:*** She doesn't see herself as unique, but as part of a whole. She doesn't dream or wonder, she just does the things that come naturally to her. She accepts the other parts of nature and feels tied to her world.

Paraphrase: The turtle is digging a hole to lay her eggs. This requires her to leave the ocean, drag herself across the sand, dig the hole, and drop her eggs in. She doesn't think much about this act; it comes naturally to her. She is a part of the chain of life in her environment, and she sees the other plants and animals. She knows that she is tied to them in the big scheme of things, but she doesn't think about it too much.

Literary Analysis SkillBuilder, page 47

Responses will vary. Possible responses are provided.

"The Elephant"

Image: a bundle of sugar-cane ***Effect:*** This helped me to see how heavy the load is that the elephant must carry.

Image: winds' untainted kiss, the waters' clean caress ***Effect:*** This helped me to picture the scene in the wild where the elephant could roam free.

Image: snap my picket-stake and forget my ankle-ring ***Effect:*** This helped me to focus on how the elephant must look now, and how he might be able to just break free and run away.

"The Turtle"

Image: dig with her ungainly feet ***Effect:*** This helped me to see how awkward it was for the turtle to dig a big hole.

Image: it came to her on the rain or soft wind ***Effect:*** This helped me to understand how instinct might work, and how the turtle just "knew" what she had to do.

Image: crawling up the high hill, luminous under the sand ***Effect:*** This helped me to see that the task ahead of her is great, and her body shines with the work.

The Elephant / The Turtle, *continued*

Follow Up: Responses will vary. Students should use the images and the effects they identified to focus their drawings. The drawings would be most effective if the students could use color in their work.

Building Vocabulary SkillBuilder

page 48

apartheid: Afrikaans : Dutch *apart,* separate from French *a part,* apart, + *-heid,* -hood; racial segregation
twin: Middle English, from Old English *twinn,* twofold; one of two babies born at the same time
freedom: Middle English *fredom,* from Old English *frēodōm*: *frēo* + *-dōm* -dom; condition of being free
vista: Italian, from feminine past participle of *vedere,* to see, from Latin *vidēre*; distant view
govern: Middle English *governen,* from Old French *governer,* from Latin *gubernāre*, from Greek *kubernan;* to make and carry out public policy
inkling: Probably an alteration of Middle English *ningkiling,* hint, suggestion, possibly alteration of *nikking,* from *nikken,* to mark a text for correction, from *nik,* notch, tally, perhaps from variant of Old French niche, *niche;* a slight hint
fugitive: Middle English *fugitif,* from Old French, from Latin *fugitīvus*, from *fugitus,* past participle of *fugere,* to flee; running away or fleeing, as from the law
gaze: Middle English *gasen,* probably of Scandinavian origin; to look steadily
character: Middle English *carecter,* distinctive mark, imprint on the soul, from Old French *caractere,* from Latin *charactēr*, from Greek *kharaktēr*, from *kharassein,* to inscribe, from *kharax,* pointed stick; qualities that distinguish one from another (and many other meanings)
nation: Middle English *nacioun,* from Old French *nation,* from Latin *nātiō*, *nātiōn-*, from *nātus*, past participle of *nāscī*, to be born; large group of people organized under a single government

from Anthony Burns: The Defeat and Triumph of a Fugitive Slave

Active Reading SkillBuilder, page 50

Responses will vary. Possible responses are provided.
Event: Henry Dana is introduced and appears in court with Burns.
Question: How can Dana oppose slavery in the North but not in the South?
Evaluate: Dana's beliefs are not consistent.
Connect: From experience, I know people are inconsistent
Clarify: Perhaps Dana's beliefs are based on his being a lawyer.
Visualize: Anthony refuses to speak because he fears Suttle.
Predict: Anthony will refuse to let Dana defend him.

Literary Analysis SkillBuilder, page 51

Responses will vary. Possible responses are provided.
Main Character: Anthony is aware of things going on around him, but he can't focus and he feels lightheaded. This shows me that Anthony is feeling weak from lack of food, as well as his hopelessness. He thinks he can never win in this system and has given up.
Other Characters: Richard Dana is persistent in following Anthony's case and in pursuing him until Anthony agrees to let Dana be his lawyer. This helps me to see how devoted Dana is to the cause and how Anthony might be gaining some hope.
Plot: The plot is basically told in the first two paragraphs. This helps me understand the context for the story and how the story fits in history. It prepares me for the events to come.
Conflict: The abolitionists versus the Fugitive Slave Law. The information about this group and this law helps me to understand the conflict in the U.S. during this time. It helps me to appreciate Anthony's story.
Dialogue: Anthony responds twice that it is no use, that Mars Charles knows him, and that his fate might be worse if he resists. This dialogue, written in Anthony's dialect, helps me to see how deep Anthony's fears and feelings of hopelessness are.

Follow Up: Responses will vary. Students should show that they understand the difference between literary nonfiction and other types of nonfiction. Students might say that they would lose personal feelings and sensory descriptions. They might mention that they could gain additional facts and background information.

Literary Analysis SkillBuilder, page 52

Responses will vary. Possible responses are provided.
Conflict: Dana opposes slavery in the North and West, but not in the South: Internal
Conflict: Anthony wants to help but is afraid to anger the colonel: Internal
Conflict: Richard Dana cannot represent Anthony if Anthony does not verbally consent to it: External
Conflict: Seth Thomas opposes the delay: External
Conflict: The proslavery and antislavery supporters were sending supporters to swing Kansas and Nebraska to their sides when they became states: External

from **Anthony Burns: The Defeat and Triumph of a Fugitive Slave,** *continued*

Grammar SkillBuilder, page 53

A. *Responses will vary. Possible responses are provided.*

1. Anthony, whose family was in Virginia, was alone in the city of Boston.
2. His hands, which had worked long and hard, were rough and callused.
3. The courtroom, which had no windows, was dark.
4. Colonel Suttle, whose face was stern and grave, sat watching Anthony.
5. The Constitution, which came from our founding fathers, is the law of the land.

B. *Responses will vary. Possible responses are provided.*
Anthony Burns, who was a former slave, thought all hope was lost. Men had come up from the South, which was where slavery was legal, to capture him. Burns's plight was familiar to many African Americans who had tried to escape slavery. Abolitionists who lived in the area tried to help. The Fugitive Slave Act, which required people to return slaves to their owners, worked against them. Antislavery feelings, which were growing rapidly, worked for them. Anthony's fate would be decided in the courthouse that was located in Boston.

Words to Know SkillBuilder, page 54

A.
1. contradict
2. throbbing
3. peer
4. petty
5. alleged

B.
1. E
2. C
3. J
4. H
5. D
6. A
7. I
8. F
9. G
10. B

Selection Quiz, page 55

Responses will vary. Possible responses are provided.

1. Burns is in Boston to get away from his master and to become a free man.
2. Anthony Burns is arrested for violating the Fugitive Slave Act. His captors feared that the Boston "radicals," local abolitionists who opposed slavery, would use whatever means possible to free him.
3. Anthony didn't want a lawyer because he thought all hope was lost and he would suffer worse punishment if he tried to fight back. He changed his mind because Dana and the reverends were so persistent and because the judge seemed to care.
4. The abolitionists were looking for another case to use in their fight against slavery. It wasn't specifically Anthony; he just happened to be in the right place at the right time.
5. The Kansas-Nebraska Bill is passed on May 25, 1854. It allows for the practice of slavery in the states carved from the two territories if it is provided for in the state constitutions. It repeals the Missouri Compromise.

The People Could Fly

Active Reading SkillBuilder, page 57

Responses will vary. Possible responses are provided.
Characters: Toby, Sarah, Driver, Overseer, Master
Conflict: The slaves want to become free. The Master, Overseer, and Driver work hard to keep them enslaved.
Time and Place: The time is before the Civil War, somewhere in the southern part of the United States, on a plantation.
Event 1: Sarah and her baby use Toby's magic to fly away.
Event 2: Toby helps other slaves to fly away, all the while making his Master angry.
Event 3: Toby flies away with all the other slaves who have wings.
Resolution: Eventually all the slaves escape or are freed, and they tell this tale over and over again as a way of remembering where they have been.

Literary Analysis SkillBuilder, page 58

Responses will vary.
Details that students invent can reveal appearance, thoughts, and feelings of their characters. Characters and details should reveal an understanding of the folk tale and its themes.

Follow Up: Responses will vary. Encourage students to follow the style of the folk tale.

Active Reading SkillBuilder, page 59

Responses will vary. Possible responses are provided.
Title: The People Could Fly
Characters: Sarah, Toby, Overseer, Driver
Conflict: Enslaved people want to be free.
Setting: A Southern plantation in the United States worked by slaves, sometime during the 17th or 18th century.

The People Could Fly, *continued*

Event 1: The Driver whipped Sarah and her baby.
Event 2: Toby says the magic words, and Sarah and her baby fly away to freedom.
Event 3: Other slaves fly away.
Event 4: The Overseer plans to kill Toby.
Event 5: Toby and many other slaves fly away to freedom.
Climax: Toby and the other slaves escape before the overseer kills Toby.
Resolution: The flight to freedom becomes a legend to those still in slavery.

Grammar SkillBuilder, page 60

Responses will vary. Possible responses are provided.

1. "Please father," Sarah pleaded, "help me to fly."
   "I'll do what I can," he responded.
2. "Shh . . . my little baby," Sarah sings softly.
3. "Did you see?" the young one asked excitedly.
   "She just took off and flew over the tree tops!"
   "It was like nothing I've ever seen," his friend added.
4. "I think we should just string him up now," the Overseer rants.
   "Now, let's think this through," the Master says.
   "We don't want to rush into it."
5. "They all took wing and flew," a small girl said.
   "I've never seen anything like it."

Words to Know SkillBuilder, page 61

A.
1. D
2. C
3. A
4. E
5. B

B.
1. snag
2. seize
3. shuffle
4. scorned
5. glinty

C. Accept responses that accurately use all **five** of the Words to Know.

Selection Quiz, page 62

Responses will vary. Possible responses are provided.

1. Toby is an old African man, and Sarah is a young African woman. Both were able to fly at one time. Now they are enslaved in America.
2. She is working in a hot field and her baby is crying from hunger. The Driver whips both Sarah and her baby. In Sarah's despair, she has forgotten how to fly.
3. Toby recites the magic words over her and she begins to fly, slowly at first, then high like a bird. The Overseer chases after her on horseback.
4. The Overseer wants to seize Toby. The Driver gets out his whip to tie him up, and the Master gets out his hip gun to kill him. Toby laughs and says the ancient words so that other people working in the field begin to fly.
5. It gives the people a sense of hope that some of them won out over the slave owners. It reminds them of their history.